Summer Gold

Afoot and light-hearted I take to the open road,
Healthy, free, the world before me,
The long brown path before me leading wherever I choose.

Henceforth I ask not good-fortune, I myself am good-fortune,
Henceforth I whimper no more, postpone no more, needing nothing,
Done with the indoor complaints, libraries, querulous criticisms,
Strong and content I travel the open road.

Walt Whitman — *Song of the Open Road*

SUMMER GOLD

A Camper's Guide To
Amateur Prospecting

John N. Dwyer

CHARLES SCRIBNER'S SONS
NEW YORK

1 3 5 7 9 11 13 15 17 19   C/C   20 18 16 14 12 10 8 6 4 2
1 3 5 7 9 11 13 15 17 19   C/P   20 18 16 14 12 10 8 6 4 2

Printed in the United States of America
Library of Congress Catalog Card Number 73–19267
ISBN 0–684–13706–2
ISBN 0–684–13719–4 (pbk.)

This book is dedicated to Richard J. Beadle and to the unnamed old-timer we met along the Feather River, whose vial of golden nuggets led me to years of pleasure and modest adventure along many rivers, and scratching among the rocks of untold abandoned mines from coast to coast.

PREFACE

This book was begun in 1943. The West coast army post was sheer boredom; I was almost broke, with a three-day pass in hand and nowhere to go. A friend, Dick Beadle, and I decided to hitchhike east to the Sierra Nevada mountains to look at some old-time gold camps. A series of rides took us to Oroville, California, where a gas station attendant advised us to go up the Feather River to Quincy, where he said gold could still be found.

We alternately rode and walked up the mountains to Quincy, passing any number of interesting side roads and trails. We arrived at Quincy during a late spring snowstorm and checked into the huge, old, barnlike hotel. After a quick clean-up, Dick and I went to the coffee shop and ordered a hearty meal. Since we were the only customers in the place, we sat and chatted with the counterman about the town and countryside around Quincy. He talked about the town as he knew it and suggested that we hike down the valley a few miles and walk along the Feather River toward Spanish Ranch and Gold Bar, which had produced gold during the placer mining days of a hundred years ago.

The next morning we had the hotelkeeper pack a lunch for us, and we headed down the valley toward Indian Falls, following the railroad tracks until we came to the river. Following the bed of an abandoned railroad, we worked our way up several small streams, stopping to examine the workings left by the placer and sluice miners. We didn't find anything of value, mainly because we didn't know what we were looking for in these creeks. We found a number of sand bars and gravel holes, but we didn't know how to work them; even if we had known, we didn't have the tools to do the job. But it was a nice walk through some beautiful mountain country.

When we returned to the hotel that evening and told the counterman about our day, he suggested that we visit the county jail and talk to the sheriff about some tools. The sheriff was a friendly man and offered to let us use a gold pan, a small shovel and pick that one of his "guests" had left with him for safekeeping. We accepted his offer and left with the borrowed tools, and headed for the main highway to hitchhike farther down the valley to another stream.

We no sooner got to the intersection of the main road and the town road when an old, battered pickup stopped to offer us a ride. The driver, a middle-aged man in coveralls and wide-brimmed felt hat, was not overly talkative as we started down the road. Dick told him that we were on an army pass and were looking for some place to try out the gold pan and our luck. The old-timer slowed down the pickup as we came to a small side creek leading off the Feather River and said that this was the most likely spot to work for specks of gold. When I told him that we had never seen gold, much less used a gold pan, he reached down and turned off the ignition. As we got out of the truck, he too left the truck and came around to our side of the road. He reached into his pocket, pulled out a small glass vial, and said, "This is gold." Inside the vial were several nuggets of shiny, worn-smooth gold and a spoonful of grains and flakes of yellow metal. He told us that this metal had come from the same creek we were standing beside, but he wouldn't tell us exactly where he had made his find. However, he did walk down the embankment with us to the edge of the stream. There he took the gold pan, knelt near a sandy-bottomed eddy in the stream, scooped up a panful of sand and gravel, and put the pan into motion.

He only stayed about fifteen minutes, making sure that we had gotten at least the crude knack of washing the pan. After a suggestion that we move a good distance upstream, since the holes near the road were regularly worked by passers-by, he clambered back up the bank, started his old pickup, and pulled away without so much as a wave.

I had asked to see the vial again before he left, but he wouldn't show us the gold again. Let me tell you now—that first and last look at the little glass bottle of gold dust set me off on a hobby that has led me to some interesting and out-of-the-way places.

Our first attempt to prospect with the borrowed pan proved less than successful. We returned to Quincy and then to our army post, as empty-handed as we had started. I returned, however, with a new and real treasure—countless hours of fun experienced since that day in the mountains. I have forgotten the count of abandoned mines and metal-producing rivers that I've visited. At each site I have spent hours gleaning the mine dumps and shoveling sand into a pan, and each hour so spent made me appreciate and love our country's history, the hardy men and women who prospected in earnest in hope of a bonanza, and, most of all, the haunting, lonely beauty of the trails and dusty roads leading into the back country.

The gold to be gotten from this book will, hopefully, be the same days of peace and adventure that I have experienced as an amateur prospector for metals. I will tell you the essential things to do to find metals; I will suggest places to go; I will show you the necessary tools; and I will give you a reading list to expand your knowledge of the subject if you find your interest increasing as you prospect. I can't flash a vial of real nuggets before your eyes, but hopefully I can pass on to you the thrill of seeing that vial and make your camping trips just that much more fun.

I would feel less than grateful if I did not take a line or two to say my thanks to some fine friends and camping companions who have added their own interest and effort in many ways to my fun as an amateur prospector. Therefore, my thanks to my wife and family for going along on some strange camping trips; to Karl Vander Horck for sharing coffee over the camp fires; to Jim Ahearn and Harold Berliner for being patient with me when I wanted to tarry at some mine dump when they had other pressing things to do; to Ervin Dix Kane, who hooked me on the wonders and fun of electronic metal detectors; to Jack Schneider, whose editorial pencil guided these words into order; and finally to my father Jim and my uncle Paul Dwyer who, perhaps unknowingly, taught me to respect and to be curious about the earth and its peoples.

Good luck, and much fun on the hunt for the main raw materials of man—metals.

JOHN N. DWYER

CONTENTS

"Panning," on the Mokelumne.

Winnowing gold, near Chinese camp.

Quicksilver machine, in Mormon Gulch.

Hydraulic Mining, at French Corral.

Summer Gold

In the days when I was hard up,
    I found a blissful hope,
It's all the poor man's heritage,
    To keep him from the rope;
But I've found a good old maxim,
    And this shall be my plan,
Altho I wear a ragged coat,
    I'll wear it like a man.

An Old Irish Song — *The Days When I Was Hard Up*

A Brief History of Gold Discovery and Mining in the United States

Gold is fascinating. Gold, along with fabled beauty, is the basis of most men's fairy tales. It has been one of the major attractions of the metal world since the dawn of history, when primitive man found the soft, malleable, shining yellow metal in the riverbeds near his dwellings.

In our day gold is a quite common metal. We find the bright stuff in the dentist's office, on the covers of books, on aircraft instruments, and picture frames. There are endless uses for gold in our modern technology, for it is one of the more stable of the metal elements known to us. Another peculiar note is that today gold is so low in value—or rather, costs are so high—that it does not really pay to establish an elaborate mining operation to extract and process the ore from the lode.

This, of course, was not true in the past. History is the keeper of the golden tale, since much of man's activity in the past was directed toward getting and keeping a horde of gold as the basis of his wealth. It might be an exaggeration to say that, pound for pound, man has given as much flesh and blood in seeking gold as the weight of all of the gold that he has obtained and held. However, I feel that it is true to say that most of the gold that comprises the world's existing monetary horde was procured by slave labor. Slave labor, in either physical or economic form, was the normal means by which the crude gold was gathered from the streams and ancient mines the world over.

Imagination is the friend of gold. Imagination transforms the soft, lovely yellow metal into works of art, symbols of marital fidelity, vessels for offerings to the gods, thread with which to weave a king's cloak or a woman's alluring dress. Imagination also lets us envision the epic of the '49ers in California; the Spanish captains fleeing full sail before the Caribbean pirates; Henry VIII fingering a golden chalice while sending wives to the sword; or modern Greek captains ordering jeweled gifts for their ladies.

Gold is valuable simply because it is a scarce ore. A metal becomes an ore only when it is available in such quantities as to make mining profitable. Today, with the exception of Russia, which uses prisoners in the state mines, and in South Africa and the Far East, where labor is plentiful and cheap, extracting the gold ore, milling and refining it, is too expensive. Thus, in the United States, which in the past has produced an enormous tonnage of gold, the cost of mining gold is far more than the value of the metal obtained. We are doing very little direct gold mining in the United States in the 1970's; almost all the metal recovered today is a by-product of another metal-mining operation.

Gold is everywhere. There is gold in your own backyard, in the creek at the edge of your town, in the natural rock which may underlie your city. Gold is plentiful in the salty oceans, and science and technology have the means of extracting even this gold. Again, it is too expensive to extract and refine at present-day gold prices. Thus we have the paradox of a metal that is very valuable because it is scarce yet plentifully spread throughout the earth but just too expensive to seek and own!

The history of the discovery and mining of gold in the United States is a long list of bonanza strikes, quick fortunes gained and lost, and many lost and broken men. The pioneers of our frontier did not break through the dense forests for their health. They were out on the dangerous land seeking what natural resources they could exploit with their raw muscle and simple tools. In addition to farming and lumbering, the early American pioneer was locating iron in Pennsylvania and Virginia, quarrying stone in the New England states, and discovering gold in North Carolina in 1799.

Most of us think of the California '49ers when we think of gold in America. However, beginning in 1799 in North Carolina, gold was discovered and worked in Georgia, Tennessee, Virginia, and along the eastern slopes of the ancient chain of mountains which are the southern Appalachians—the Blue Ridge and Smokey Mountains. For example, from 1799 until 1960, the larger mining operations in North Carolina alone produced over $6,100,000 worth of gold from such mines as Kings Mountain, Russell, Hoover Hill, Honeycutt, Union Copper, and others in Burke, Gaston, Montgomery, and Rown Counties. It should be noted that some of these mines have not been worked for over a hundred years. The Civil War put an end to the mining, and these mines have lain idle since that conflict. There have been prospectors working the area during the passing years, seeking the signs that might lead them to the large-scale pay dirt or lode. However, most of the Eastern mines, including the Cornwall in Pennsylvania, have not been worked for gold in many decades. It is an interesting fact that our genius president, Thomas Jefferson, made the earliest written reference to gold in the colonial United States when he recorded that the metal had been found along the Rappahannock River in 1782.

The gold strikes in Georgia in the 1830's and 1840's were beginning to play out when the Sutter gold discovery in California made news along the Eastern seaboard. The new lands to the west spelled riches to the bottled-up Eastern settlers. They eagerly sought new lands to work, especially lands in which every river was brimful of solid gold nuggets for the picking. As the oft-repeated story went, all a man had to do was to get to California, fill a knapsack full of large golden boulders, and hurry back home to settle down with a paid-up farm, cattle, and a wife. It was the same old dream which has always drawn men to new frontiers—they just changed the names of the rivers and hills and doubled the size of the potential wealth.

It is not necessary to go into the details of how all the prospectors got to California; history books are full of the wild tales of wagon trains, ships sailing around the Horn, and buckskinned trailriders, all racing like greyhounds to be the first to the diggings. And what diggings! The mountains of California, formed by continuous geologic upheavals, rent with jagged fissures through the bedrock, had been storing gold in the broken rock for eons. Additional eons of time furnished the snows and rains needed to wash the metal loose from the mother rock, rinse it down to the riverbeds, and store it in the gravelly pockets along the rivers and outwash plains of a hundred rivers along the whole of the West coast.

This was a bonanza—a territory-wide bonanza! There was plenty of gold for everyone who made it through the desert and Indian country to the Sierra passes or who survived the scurvy and breakbone fever to land in the gold-mad town of San Francisco. The rush brought the usual collection of roughs and criminals, but most of the seekers were dedicated, hard-working family men who wanted to make a stake and return home with a handsome purse gained from a few months of hard work on the placers. Again, we will leave it to the history books to record the details of pain, loss, hurt, and success brought by the wealth of the Mother Lode. Suffice it to say the '49 gold rush survived the murderous Sidney Ducks, the Black Barts, and the jumping frogs to become a big business which lasted until high costs ended serious gold production in the late 1940's and early 1950's. There are, of course, working mines in the California hills even today, but they are mostly one-man and two-men operations. There, too, you can still meet the prospector searching the mountains and rivers for another Grass Valley-Nevada City lode.

I will try to give some small idea of the wealth which lay in the Sierra Nevada Mountains when the real gold rush started in 1848. Most Americans think that Sutter's decision to build a mill, and Marshall's chance finding of nuggets in the stream, was the first discovery of gold in California. This was not the case, for the Spaniards had done some modest mining during the two hundred years before Sutter even knew Marshall. Before the Spaniards came, the Indians of the coastal area had worked the streams for the bits of shiny yellow metal to use as trade items and bright decorations.

Americans were ready to travel across the bleak plains and settle on the rich lands of the West. Stories had come back to the East telling how beautiful and provident the Western lands were for settlers. The rich Sutter Mill gold discovery proved to be the key. And believe it— there *was* a bonanza in California! The Mother Lode district in Amador County produced over $25,000,000 in bullion, most of it mined within ten years of the Sutter Mill strike. Another true bonanza was the Grass Valley-Nevada City diggings, where the Empire and North Star Lode

Helvetia Quartz Mill, Grass Valley.

mines, along with the <u>placers and hydraulics on the Yuba River</u>, yielded a quarter of a billion dollars! Nevada County was the answer to an eager prospector's prayer. Only three other districts in the United States have out-produced this rich valley—Lead, South Dakota, with its Homestake Mine, and the Cripple Creek district of Colorado, and Carlin, Nevada. It is almost beyond belief to think that an area approximately twenty by thirty miles could be so rich in the gold ore wealth of Mother Earth.

The Mother Lode and the Grass Valley diggings were the most productive of the California prospects. The gold production area of that state extended from the San Diego area (and even inside the present area of Los Angeles) northward to the Harrison Gulch and Whiskeytown diggings in Shasta County. California was truly a gifted state, blessed with good land, sunshine, water for crops and cattle, and literally tons of gold and silver to ease the problems of getting the capital needed for growth.

As the various California mining areas were worked out, or claim-staked, the now experienced prospectors turned eastward. The mountain men of the 1820's and 1830's had talked of gold they had seen in the Rocky Mountain streams when they came in from their trap lines to the annual trade rendezvous. The fur trappers' tales were retold around the California gold camps, and some of the more adventurous miners shouldered their prospecting kits and began to work in the streams of Idaho and Montana. During these same years the soldiers stationed at the primitive forts in Montana and Idaho did some prospecting during their idle hours. Soon the reports of good "color" began to call more and more men to the Montana and Idaho discovery areas.

Reports from the Clearwater River area east of Fort Walla Walla, in the Nez Percé Indian country of Idaho, told of much gold. Soon the Oro Fino and Pierce diggings were going full tilt. So too, the Montana prospectors found at Bannack the bonanza waters of Grasshopper Creek.

The ruins of the head frame, crushing mill and mining camp at Bannack, Montana — The Grasshopper Creek Diggin's.

At Virginia City, on Alder Greek and the Ruby River, the placers were teeming with eager miners from the East and from the California gold fields.

The Idaho placers were rich, and the lode mines were almost as rich. The General Custer mine in Custer County reported $8,000,000 in bullion; the Red Warrior in Gem County turned in $1,000,000; and the owners of the Yellow Jacket and DeLamar mines in Owyhee County reveled in a lode worth $23,000,000.

The Montana gold fields were much richer than those of Idaho. During the 103 years from 1862 until 1965, the placer workings of Montana produced over 9,000,000 ounces of fine gold worth $180,000,000. The lode mines of Montana provided the prospectors and speculators with an additional $170,000,000 in gold. A third of a billion dollars from one state! It is safe to say that Thomas Jefferson, with a kind of unknowing foresight, really made the buy of the century when he concluded the Louisiana Purchase from France.

The names of a few of the richer mines from the Montana fields will give you an idea of the imagination of the miners when it came to naming a mine or claim. A very productive one was the Drumlummon mine at Marysville, in Lewis and Clark County, which gave its owners a total of $9,000,000 from its operation. This mine, the stamping mill, the reducing plant, and the "ghost town" are still there for the visitor and prospector to examine. The North Moccasin district and the North

The Drumlummon mine works; ore dump, crusher, head frame, and cyanide mill. The trestle leads from the mine to the abandoned railroad bed.

Mocassin mine in Fergus County tallied a total of $8,500,000 for its working life. The Scratch Gravel Mine had a lode worth $11,000,000. Other million–dollar mines were found and worked in Deer Lodge, Granite, Jefferson, and Madison Counties.

Again, the miner who had not hit his pay dirt or who was idle began to roam the areas of Wyoming and Colorado. Wyoming did not have the broken, fractured mountains in which nature stores lodes of gold. Wyoming's bonanza came later with the discovery of huge oil, gas, coal, and uranium fields. The miners and prospectors drifted southward, prospecting through the passes, into Colorado. Again, Lady Luck turned her favor upon the prospector. The rivers showed the yellow of pay placers, and the Colorado rush was on in earnest. Colorado ranks second in gold production through 1965 with a total of some 41,000,000 ounces of gold worth $820,000,000 or better than three quarters of a billion dollars! The first nugget found in the Central City area west of present-day Denver was the miner's call to a giant-sized payday! The Cripple Creek Mining Camp, as it was called, was the largest single strike area in Colorado. This district alone gave up some 19,00,000 ounces of gold, or about half of the total gold output of the entire state.

Again the colorful names pop up when we look to see which mines were the real producers. The Last Chance, in Mineral County, in addition to having a colorful personality as its owner (Leadville Johnny Brown), produced $1,500,000, as well as the story idea for the very successful modern musical comedy, *The Unsinkable Molly Brown*. The Liberty Bell mine, in San Miguel County, brought in a ringing $12,660,000, while its neighbor, the Silver Pick, worked out a modest $500,000 in shiny yellow bullion. Another pay dirt mountain was in Animas County in the Eureka District, well-named the Gold King mine, out of which was dug, crushed, and refined a total of $10,000,000 in fine gold.

The development of gold prospecting in other areas was delayed by marauding Indian bands in Arizona, the forbidding deserts of Nevada, Indian warfare, and the difficult distances for transport in Oregon and Washington. These areas, however, have added substantially to the history and lore of gold and silver mining in the United States.

Briefly, Arizona prospecting was hindered by the fierce and brave defense which the Apache and other tribes made to save their homelands.

Many a prospector's bones bleached in the sun because of his foolish venturing into the outlands of Arizona. Arizona's gold and silver history has well recorded the efforts of the Spanish, using Indian slave labor, to dig gold from the harsh and mysterious Sangre de Cristo Mountains. Most of the gold which has been produced in Arizona has come as a by-product of the refining of other metal ores, mainly the rich copper ores from the Bisbee area.

Arizona, too, produced some colorfully named mines—the Christmas mine, in Gilas County, which issued $500,000 in ore; the Vulture mine, in Maricopa County, which came in with almost $2,000,000 in earnings; the Fortuna, in Yerma County, worth $2,500,000 in fine gold; and the Gold Bar and Octave mines, in Yavapai County, which produced over $2,000,000. It is interesting to note that all of the mining done specifically for gold does not come anywhere near reaching the total of gold production as a by-product from the processing of other metal ores. The Bisbee district of Arizona alone has returned to its investors (mainly the Phelps-Dodge Corporation) better than $24,000,000 in gold since 1880 as a by-product of copper mining.

No gold history would be complete without mentioning the famous Comstock mine in Nevada. This lode mine, in Storey County, has produced $160,000,000, much of it as a by-product of the very rich silver workings, which earned more than the gold bullion. The Comstock mine is also famous for the endless litigation and ill-luck which dogged the mine's early producing years. Other valuable Nevada mining properties lay close to, and north of, the deadly arid deserts which comprise the alkalai salt sands of Death Valley, of Twenty-Mule Team fame. This lonely, arid mining area attracted the prospectors who discovered the pay dirt placers in Esmeralda, Clark, and Nye Counties. Representative mines of value from these counties are the Quartette mine, worth almost $3,000,000, the Shoshone mine, in the Bullfrog district, which gave up $2,500,000 in pay ore; and the Mohawk mine, in the Goldfield district, which produced a staggering $84,000,000! In northern Nevada, the Getchell mine, in Humboldt County, gave the miners—or I should say, the investors—the tidy sum of $8,000,000 for their risk. You should remember the Comstock, and visit the mine site if you are in that area of Nevada, for it was one of the grand glory holes of United States mining history. The still-working Carlin mine, in the Independence

Mountains of southwestern Elko County, has become, as of 1970, the second largest gold mine in North America, and there is still $100,000,000 in micro nuggets to dig from that great, open pit mine!

The average American would never think of Oregon or Washington in terms of gold and silver mining. These two states, however, did have their moments of glory in the history of prospecting and mining. As was mentioned earlier, the hostile resentment of the Indians over the white prospectors invading their tribal lands and the difficult transportation of supplies and machinery delayed the development of mining in these two states. We can note that Oregon had several good mining areas, representative of which is the North Pole Mine, in Baker County, from which was carved some $9,000,000 in good, high-grade gold. There were several other million-dollar mines in Oregon, such as the Virtue, Rainbow, and the Connor Creek mines, in Baker County; and the Ashland and the Steamboat mines, in Jackson County. Farther north, in Washington, along the Moses Coulee and Okanogan Range in Chelan County, the Holden and the Gold King mines produced $14,000,000; farther north, toward the Canadian border, the $16,000,000 mining complex of Republic-Knob Hill, in Ferry County, was worked for some years.

A history of gold mining in the United States must begin or end with the geographically small but ungodly rich South Dakota mine at Lead, in Lawrence County, known worldwide as that granddaddy of all bonanzas, the Homestake mine. This mine, which is still working and producing gold and silver on daily shifts, has produced, from its opening in 1875 until 1969, a total of $735,000,000 in gold alone! This is by far the largest and richest gold mine ever worked in the United States. A visitor to the Black Hills of western South Dakota can join any of several daily tourist tours conducted by the corporation operating this vast mine. South Dakota has produced some 8,000,000 additional ounces of gold from the very small mining area of Lawrence and Pennington Counties. Deadwood Gulch of boot hill cemetery fame, was the first rich placer area discovered, and gave forth to the early prospectors who worked the virgin gravel the tidy sum of $8,000,000. This area is not only beautiful country in which to camp, but you can share the violent history represented by General George Custer, Wild Bill Hickok, and Calamity Jane Canary.

Understandably, since this is a guide to amateur prospecting, the history of gold hunting is nowhere complete, nor does this book pretend to be exhaustive on the subject. Added to the end of this book is a reading list to direct interested readers to additional information and technical detail. I presume that the amateur would want to seek specific prospecting information concerning the area of the country in which he will do his camping, and perhaps after reading this little volume, he will wet a gold pan. I have not included Alaska, which, although it is a state, is not an area commonly traveled by the average camper.

In bringing this brief history of gold prospecting and mining in the United States to a close, it might be well to recap the total picture of gold ores and mining in this country. The amount of gold discovered and mined profitably in the United States has totaled, from 1799 through 1965, some 307,000,000 ounces of raw gold, with a total value of $10,750,000,000. This treasure, which greatly added to our nation's wealth during its Civil War and westward expansion days, was gleaned mainly from twenty-one states, each of whose total production exceeded 10,000 ounces of gold.

Almost every state in the union has at one time or another had a small-scale gold rush. I mentioned earlier that gold is everywhere, and almost every state has produced small pockets of gold for the eager prospector to hunt. Michigan, Wyoming, Minnesota, Alabama are just a few states that enjoyed small, brief, but boisterous gold-fever booms. Michigan had a good mine working near Marquette, in the Upper Peninsula, called the Ropes mine. This mine was peculiar, since it was only a small pocket of gold ore which lay between the rich iron ore deposits of the Marquette Range and the equally rich float and vein copper mines at Houghton. Minnesota made a small and not too profitable claim to gold mining glory with the establishment of the Rainy Lake City diggings near International Falls. The Rainy Lake City diggings laid claim to three mines—the Bushyhead, Big America, and Dryweed Islands—at least five log saloons, and five stamping mills. It was a roaring town, but since it was a ninety-mile pack trip through the brush to take the small amount of gold out, and the same distance to return with supplies, it faded fast. Farther east, on Lake Vermillion, another small island mine was worked with no real success.

Read on, friend, for the fun of prospecting is in the anticipation.

The ghosttown main street of Marysville, Montana. This is the site of the famous Drumlummon mine.

At the foot of the Judith mountains, near the ghost town of Giltedge, Montana, sits the ruins of a stone and sod house which sheltered the miners who worked in the Giltedge Diggin's.

The well preserved ruins of the old two story school house in Marysville.

A beautiful old log miner's cabin at the 1863 gold workings at Garnet, Montana. The cabin site is high above the steep roadway called the "Chinee Grade."

The old town jail, with solid log roof and sidewalls, which held the members of the infamous Plummer gang before they were hung on the hillside overlooking the Grasshopper Creek Diggin's.

Where To Go To Prospect
For Gold, Silver and Other Metals

First of all, it should be obvious to any amateur prospector that without a deep and professional training in geology or mining, any genuine gold strike will be sheer accident. The professional geologists and professional mining people, using the most sophisticated tools of modern technology, have spent millions in conducting surveys to locate likely prospect areas. The federal and various state governments have carried out systematic reporting programs, both projective and reflective, in an effort to make reasonable forecasts as to the location and extent of reserve mineral wealth left in the care of the commonwealth.

It is here that I make the point for the amateur prospector. The amateur is not looking for huge beds or veins of ore which call for the investment of major capital monies; he is simply spending some vacation days, at his own expense, pursuing a rather intriguing hobby. It is true that this may pay off in the making of a real strike, but his main purpose is recreational. If the gold fever gets to the amateur to the extent that he starts thinking of prospecting as a way of life, he'd best remember those bleached bones lying on the desert floor. That prospector wasn't necessarily done in by violence, but just up and died from hunger because he pushed his luck and grubstake too far.

With this warning out of the way, we can now talk about where to go to prospect for gold, silver, or other metals. It is fairly obvious from the preceding section that you could try a panful of gravel in almost any stream east and south of the mountains which set off Virginia and the Southeast from the Northern states, especially the southeastern corner of Tennessee, the rivers of the central section of the Carolinas, and the easy-flooding rivers of central Virginia, and central Georgia and Alabama. Reference to the major mining areas of these states noted in the appendix and the use of a good atlas will clue you toward the areas which will likely show color in your gold pan. There are some areas in these states in which the landowners have set up a "pay and pan" system, whereby a small fee allows one to pan for gold or valuable mineral gems along their creek and river right of ways. There is very little public land left in these areas, and, of course, the national and state park services get downright nasty if they find you digging in the precious soil of their public preserves.

The more fortunate prospectors are those who live in the Middlewestern or far Western states. They have a much easier time getting to areas that are good prospecting lands. Almost any spot west of the 100° latitude that has a good campsite and fresh water is good for a try at "color."

However, to be realistic, most of the gold deposits found in the United States have been the result of geologic changes in the ancient country rock dating from the geologic period of the Jurassic to the Tertiary formations—roughly from the beginning of the formation of the Sierra Nevada mountains some two hundred million years ago to

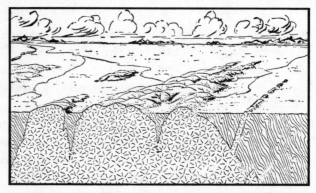

A batholith intrusion which has pushed up through the ancient bedrock to form an outcrop on the surface of the surrounding level plain. This batholith is fifty miles wide.

the final formation of the Rocky Mountains some one million years ago. These vast geologic disturbances, which forced the old bedrock upward, caused breaks in the bedrock which allowed the lower interior molten rocks (magma) to push upward batholiths (a kind of vast bell-shaped formation of igneous rocks), stocks (same shape as a batholith but much smaller in mass—up to ten miles in diameter), and satellitic intrusive bodies (a fancy way of saying veins, fissures, cracks, and the like). The interior core materials of the earth were very hot, and thus many minerals passed into a super-heated gaseous or steam state. These vapors, being hot and light in weight, worked their way up toward the surface through cracks or fissures in the faulted (broken) rock. As the hot gases reached the upper or surface levels, they cooled and condensed along the native rock walls in the pockets and veins caused by the faults.

A piece of ore rock containing massive quartz crystals which have formed in a wild, random pattern. This specimen contained wire gold.

Since most elemental materials form crystals in their pure form, the metals tend to form crystals with similar molecular materials. Thus, gold molecules are attracted to one another to form crystals. So, too, do the other metals form their deposits. Thus, within the massive formations of quartz crystals, which are the most common form of deposit, the prospector will find pockets, veins, vugs, and perhaps even beds of the metal ore he is seeking. In the practical world of prospecting, much of the gold and silver ores are found to have formed in combination with other minerals as the cooling process deposited these minerals in the fissures in the walls of the country rock.

Generally, these so-called secondary ore deposits are very difficult, if not impossible, for the amateur prospector to work. The tools, machines, and chemicals needed to mine, crush, and separate these ore salts are too expensive and unmanageable for the lone camper or prospector. There are small testing kits available which will allow you to perform small-scale crushing and refining tests to determine the nature of the ore material. These field assay kits are best left to the more experienced prospector.

The normal geologic deposits that are of interest to weekend gold panners are the alluvial deposits. These are the placer deposits that nature has kindly left for us to find. We might find gold in the surface holes or pockets where the metals have been enriched by natural erosion, i. e., left to gather in the hollows of harder rocks as the softer metal-bearing rocks were washed away during the breakdown of the rock by sun, snow, rain, and wind. The gold and silver, being much heavier than the silicas which commonly form the rock, sink to the bottom of the trap or hole as the eroded material is blown and washed away.

The amateur prospector has likely formed some idea in his mind as to what raw gold looks like. He perhaps expects all the gold in the rocks and streams to be granular. I think you should remember here that gold is where you find it, and it seems to come in any form your imagination can dream up for it. Usually, gold is free of other mineral combinations by the time it has reached the placers. The salts of the various chemicals which might have been combined with the gold in the bedrock have dissolved, and the gold has been rubbed and pounded smooth by the eroding action of the water and from tumbling among the rocks of the placer stream. The color of gold is yellow, a soft, almost grease-like yellow, a color and texture which are very hard to mistake if you sincerely do not want to be fooled. The only other common materials that could deceive you are mica and iron pyrites, or "fool's gold." However, since fool's gold is brittle, flaky, and light in weight and tends to tarnish quickly, the amateur prospector will soon have a feeling and eye for this imposter.

For descriptive purposes, I will use the terms generally used by the professional prospector and miner to describe the kinds of gold you will likely find in placer deposits, pockets, or veins. *Flour gold*, as the name implies, is very fine and just as slippery as the flour used to bake your cakes. The size of the flour grains is very small, for as they become larger, the description changes to coarse gold. *Coarse gold* ranges in size from rather large specks to pinhead size to nuggets that might weigh hundreds of pounds. If, by some chance of luck or fate, you ever find a large nugget or gold boulder of several pounds, call me on the telephone and share your happiness with me, for you can afford it. Frankly, I don't expect too many calls to disturb my life. The two above-mentioned forms of gold are usually found in placers or streams. You might also find two other forms of gold metal—*leaf* and *wire*. These are self-explanatory and will be no problem for you to identify when you locate them. These last two forms are likely to be found only in veins or bed structure, where the gold has formed in the small cracks in the quartz rocks and has not been broken or changed by erosion.

One final sign for which the prospector should be alert. Remember that our earth is a living thing, in the sense that it is always moving and forming new structures within and on its surface. Therefore, ancient rock formations are constantly changing, and it is even possible for more recent rock formations to undergo changes in their composition. It is possible to find rock which has been fractured, in which the ancient fissure has been filled with some mineral deposit, and the old vein refractured to be filled again with another mineral of later deposit. This is why I like to think of geology as an art rather than a science. We know what Mother Earth is supposed to do, but she sometimes pulls other tricks. This is what makes prospecting not only fascinating but also frustrating. What seems like a good mineral deposit for mining might turn out to be a petered-out vein that has been replaced with some other less interesting or less valuable material. This is what makes people go broke in the highly speculative mining business.

We have briefly covered the hows of gold formation and the whys and wheres of its present location. We must remember that gold and all minerals and earth structures are on the move. The beginning amateur will naturally assume that since he is standing on the bank of a fine stream or creek in the midst of historical gold country, all he need do is shovel gravel into his pan and wash out the cost of his trip. He doesn't really know yet how to seek gold, and he has not yet established the instinctive awareness of the land which a prospector needs. If our prospector were to look behind himself, he would discover that although he is standing on the edge of a fine stream of water, he may have pitched his tent and built his fire on the edge of an ancient river bank. The gravel he should be working in his pan might more profitably come from the older stream bed rather than from the later one. Remember how many millions of years have passed while the place deposits have been forming.

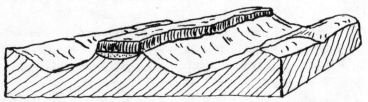

Illustration showing a modern river valley system which has cut through an ancient river bed high above the present plain. The ancient river was covered with an outflow of lava, and buried.

This is not to say that you should not try the present-day stream course, but look around to see where the river course was centuries and eons ago. In many cases the ancient river bank might be hundreds of feet above the present-day river. One riverbank I remember well. I had done just what I've described. I had worked my way up a stream, found a likely looking sand bar below a bend in the stream, and had pitched my camp on a grassy ledge about thirty feet above the river because it was a beautiful spot. After a fruitless day of working my sand bar and several holes above and below the camp, I had planned to move higher up the mountain the following morning. That evening while sitting at the edge of my camp, with my feet dangling over the steep edge, I was admiring the scene. Like the fabled thunderbolt striking, I suddenly realized that my camp had been pitched for a whole day on the bank of an ancient river. I was mad, embarrassed with myself, and finally delighted. The next two days were spent lugging pails of gravel from along the old bed for testing. I had a great deal of fun, a great deal of hard work, and a little deal of gold. The old, untouched gravel held gold, but only enough to give me traces of color. I spent further days working along the old stream bed looking for the color to increase and encourage me. But time ran out, and I had to forego any further exploration of that river. It was a good experience, though, and made me realize that I had to look around very carefully to size up the country-side before choosing a place to pull a prospect.

What all of this amounts to is that the prospector should be alert. He should be aware of the land around him as he moves through the prospect territory he has chosen. He should see the mountains and rivers, not just look at them. His eye should be trained to notice old water-courses, to observe any unusual depressions in the surrounding area. Be alert! He should check out any sink holes to see if he can fathom the reason for the unusual formation. The prospector's eyes should scan the land to catch any unusual formations or strange coloration among the rocks. His search should be alert for any unusual tree or growth formation or coloration which might suggest certain mineral content in the surface soil.

The prospector will be more than rewarded by an increased aware-ness of his land, its formations, and color. His camping trips will take on a kind of low key excitement because of the anticipation of finding something somewhere which no one else has ever found. These dis-coveries are especially satisfying if he knows that the prospect area has been worked over before, but because of his skill he came up the winner.

I would suggest that you plan to do your first prospecting in areas where proven placers or mines have been worked in the past. The list of mines in the appendix or a look at the map which marks the major gold strike areas will suggest sites nearby which can be a starting point. It would be well, too, to make a visit to your state's school of mines, and to the natural history or historical society to view their collection of minerals and metals. This will provide a basis for making comparisons with the mineral material your prospect could uncover. These institu-tions will help the amateur on a casual basis, but they will not be interested in helping provide a commercial evaluation of mineral pros-pects. They will suggest that the advice of consulting geologists or assay-ers be gotten to provide an evaluation of a mineral find. This is good advice, and these services can be obtained in most of the larger towns in the Western part of the United States. In some areas, faculty members from the school of mines will do private geologic consulting work on a fee basis.

The state historical museums in Helena, Montana, and Denver, Colorado, have interesting collections of gold samples taken from all the mining districts of the state. The museum of the School of Mines, Rapid City, South Dakota, has a most informative and attractive mineral collection. Through visits to the state museum and universities, the prospector can become familiar with the structure, color, and composition of the various minerals associated with gold and silver. In all areas in which gold can be found there will be other forms of associated mineralization which may include lead, copper, zinc, and cinnabar, plus mineralization in the form of crystal structures which will give semiprecious gems, industrial minerals such as garnet and other minerals of value.

Another aspect of amateur prospecting that some campers overlook is the economic and hobby value of collecting antique items from abandoned mine and town sites. There is a fairly good market in the United States for old bottles, old firearms, snuff and tobacco containers, tools, lighting devices and fixtures, and other so-called collectables. I would hesitate to assign any values to any of these items, since the market for them depends upon a meeting of the minds of the buyer and seller.

In my personal collection I have an old miner's lamp, a candle spike which was driven into the wooden shoring and used to hold a candle or taper to light the mine shafts, mine-car wheels, pieces of mine-car rails, picks, spikes, shovels, star drills, beautiful bottles, and bits of this and that. All these items were picked up in abandoned areas. Do not, under any circumstances, take anything from working mine areas, from posted properties, or from the buildings in old ghost towns. The normal vandalism of our citizens has wrecked all too many fine old buildings in these historic areas. We should all make an effort to preserve what is left of our mining heritage.

As a personal interest, you might find working old mine dumps or tipple piles for unusual rock formations a very satisfying means of prospecting. Many of the old mine dump areas, including coal and iron mines, contain small bits of crystal formations, petrified plant life, fossil remains, and ore samples. Since many of the Western mine dumps were

The remains of a once handsome double house near Giltedge, Montana.

reworked once or twice by Chinese laborers, there is little likelihood of finding any valuable ore samples in these areas. However, the old prospectors and the Chinese laborers were not too interested in collecting examples of crystal forms and simply ignored this type of mineral.

I personally feel that Montana has the most varied offerings for the amateur prospector. There are a large number of abandoned or closed mine areas in this state. Scattered throughout the state are interesting ghost, or near-ghost, towns that the camper-prospector could work for bottles and collectable items. I once found several old liquor and milk bottles at an abandoned mine dump located about eight thousand feet up on the side of a mountain in the Judith Mountain range. I had read of the mine in an old book and had located the site on an old government chart. It was not too difficult to find the overgrown wagon trail leading up the side of the mountain, but it proved far more difficult to locate the actual mine. On that trip I had to be satisfied with finding the location of the living quarters and dump area, from which I uncovered some handsome bottles.

In addition to mines and ghost towns, Montana offers many good possible locations for placer or gold panning attempts. The rivers of Montana, as well as the hills, offer additional possibilities for finding gem stones, agates, and jade. The final plug I wish to make for Montana is that the people are friendly, the country is beautiful, and the camping, for the most part, is excellent.

An old time ore wagon used with horses or oxen to haul ore rock from the mine head to the crusher, or stamp mill. This wagon is in the town of Lewistown, Montana.

Southeastern, south, and west central Idaho are a prospector's delight. However, the landscape is rugged, and much of the countryside is either back- or animal-packing area, or only suited for all-terrain vehicles such as jeeps and four-wheel-drive pickups with very high undercarriage clearance. The south central area of Idaho is rich in volcanic formations. The Craters of the Moon National Monument area, which is worth any camper's time, is a good area in which to make a search of the land. To the north and west of the Craters of the Moon is an old silver and copper mining area. The countryside around Chilly, Mackay, and Darlington has old mines that can be dump-worked. The southwest corner of Idaho is another area rich in mining history. The ghost towns of DeLamar and Silver City, and others provide a good spot for prospecting or antique hunting. I might warn you that this area is not for your loaded-down family car and fold-down camper trailer with their very low highway clearance.

Most of the mining areas in Washington, Oregon, and California can be reached with relative ease. You can take your fancy camping gear to these areas, set up in local state or national forest campgrounds, and make your way to the mine areas by car and foot. You should have some lightweight prospecting gear, about which we will talk in the next section.

Colorado and some parts of eastern Utah also offer easy access for automobiles. However, you should be very careful when going into the dry and rugged areas of western Utah, Nevada, Arizona, and New Mexico. If you are just beginning to become interested in metal prospecting, it would be best to stick to good roads, settled areas, and convenient sources of supplies and help. The more isolated areas of the Southwest are best left to those who have had a good deal of experience in handling the special problems which can arise in the desert and off-road locations.

For those who would like to try their hand at prospecting in the East, there are always the old iron and coal mines in Pennsylvania and West Virginia. The very old gold workings and gem streams in the Southeast are always sources of try-your-luck prospecting. Most of the Northeastern states have quarry areas that will yield most satisfying samples of rock for a good collection. In some cases, there have been some valuable and startling finds of gem stones in Maine, Vermont, New Jersey, and New York. The Upper Peninsula of Michigan is a treasure trove of interesting old mine areas. The Keweenaw Peninsula, in the region of Houghton and Ontonagan, will provide many good days of camping and hunting for bits and pieces of float copper. This is one of the few areas in the world where pure copper was found—copper which had been freed by erosion and the leaching out of its accompanying mineral companions. This whole area of Michigan is covered with both open pit and deep shaft iron and copper mines. It is fun to search the dumps of these mines for crystals, iron ore samples, and other mineralizations.

The iron mines of Wisconsin, both central and northern, and of northern Minnesota provide excellent camping and equally excellent ore sampling. The north shoreline of Lake Superior in Minnesota is rich in agate and thompsonite mineral beaches. Natural agate can be one of the most beautiful of all minerals. Western Illinois and Eastern Missouri are not the greatest summer-camping areas, but there the prospector will find coal, lead, and zinc mines. The dumps of some of the lead mines in Missouri yield beautiful crystals of galena, which is the crystal formation of lead.

I have saved what I believe to be a very important point for the very end of this section so that you will remember it well and be saved no end of trouble. *Remember well* that this is a country which has high public respect for personal and private property. This is especially true where the landowner is a local citizen of some importance and the trespasser is a summer visitor from out of state! Keep out of places that are marked "private property" or "no trespassing." Stay out of areas marked by the federal government as restricted—these federal lads get very touchy about citizens wandering around inside bombing and gunnery ranges, or weapon-testing sites (Nevada is a great area for such restrictions). There are vast areas of public forest and grazing lands in the West which are open for public use by amateur prospectors. Again, though, the government is a little testy about professional prospecting in certain publicly held lands.

The most simple way to handle the problem of private property is to ask for permission from the owner or guardian to enter upon the property for personal hobby purposes. If the area is so isolated that you cannot locate boundary lines, owners, or caretakers nearby, it might be safe to enter unfenced creek beds from a highway to wet your gold pan. This is not a real worry, for there are more places for you to go than not to go. Do not engage in open violation of another's property and goods. Remember, too, that all buildings—especially old buildings—are part of our history and should be preserved. Please do not become a member of that disrespectful band of travelers who assume that everything not tied down is theirs—these are the vandals of our modern times.

The old three story hotel in the remote ghost town of Garnet. The rooms are still covered with a beautiful floral wall paper pattern. The hotel was built about 1875.

The drooping, and soon-to-go livery stable at Garnet, Montana.

A typical abandoned mine scene in the mountains of Western United States.

The old clapboard church and log parsonnage in the territorial capitol of the Montana Territory—Bannack.

Prospecting Tools
and How to Use Them in the Field

The Tools You'll Need

In theory, all that is needed to find some placer gold, besides luck, is an old, burned-out frying pan. History has recorded a couple interesting strikes which have been made with a frying pan. As a matter of fact, one bonanza find was made by a mule's shoe accidentally striking the moss from a lode vein which had reached the surface.

Practically speaking, however, it is necessary for even an amateur prospector to have a good set of tools with which to do his work. If for nothing else, a well-blackened iron prospector's pan and a small vial of gold dust are good for a whole winter of bragging back home. What constitutes a good set of basic tools for a man to have along on his camping prospect?

Surprisingly, the cost of a basic set of tools is almost next to nothing. A gold pan, preferably a large fourteen- or sixteen-inch one, costs only a couple of dollars. Some suppliers will sell a complete prospecting kit, with basic equipment, for as little as six or seven dollars. This basic kit will contain, in addition to the gold pan, a pocket magnifying glass of eight or ten power, a horseshoe magnet, and a couple of clear plastic vials in which to carry your gold or assay sample. Other tools can be added to your basic kit as you find need for them. The photos accompanying this section will guide your choice.

From experience, I would suggest that a camper's prospecting kit should contain, in addition to the above items, a prospector's hammer—the kind which has a pick point; a heavy (two or three pound) short-handled hammer, called a moil or single jack, to crush rock for panning, to drive claim stakes, hammer the rock drill, and the like; a short D-handled shovel to dig gravel and sand, as well as to provide a sanitary aid if you're camping off the trail. If your kit weight will allow it, you might take along a small miner's pick with a fixed handle. This is a kind of specialized item and might have to be purchased in Western mining areas or in an antique shop in a coal or iron region. This pick is about two-thirds as large as a regular road-gang pickaxe, and it is a real pleasure to use because it handles so easily.

To the above basic tools I would add two or three long cold chisels, or gads (the diamond and cape point kind); a large-opened sieve or hand screen (for gem and rock collection); a short pry bar of good quality. Again, I would add another pry bar if your weight limit allows, for two pry bars will allow you to exert opposing pressures upon fractures in bedrock, thus giving you a chance to force an opening in the bed for your prospecting purposes. An additional useful item to have along is a small field notebook in which to jot down your daily notes during your prospect. A record of events and details might prove useful later to back a claim for which you have entered a file.

A very simple set of prospecting tools: pack, electronic metal finder, gold pan, safety hat, pick, compass, chisels or gads, prospect hammer, magnifying glass, horseshoe magnet, D-handle shovel, pry bars. All of these tools are easily packed and carried by one man.

Needless to say, you should have a good—and I mean good—compass. I would recommend a <u>Brunton.</u> You should know how to use the compass, and you should protect this instrument as you would your own life. Detailed maps for use with the compass are a must. Without good maps you will simply end up wandering about in your selected territory in a random, non-productive way. Good maps of almost all areas of interest can be had for a modest fee from <u>map dealers or the federal government.</u> The large-scale government maps of the Western states are magnificent. <u>The address of the federal map service is listed in the appendix</u>.

A few additional personal and safety supplies should complete the basic prospecting needs for the average camper. A <u>plastic safety hat</u>—the kind worn by construction workers—is a good item to have when you are working in an area which possibly has loose rock along the valley walls above your head. If you wear glasses, take a second pair along in your kit. It would be hard to make your way on some remote back-country trail without good eyesight to guide you. Heavy <u>leather workgloves</u> are a blessing when you handle sharp rock.

Some safety tips for the camper-prospector cannot be repeated too often. Your camping gear and prospecting kit should be checked often to see that it is complete and in operating condition. We all seem to forget to take along those things that make a trip comfortable, beneficial, and relaxing. We forget our ponchos to ward off the rain; we forget to take along a toilet kit, thus making our outing something less than sensational; we forget a good insect repellant and spend too much time fighting gnats and bugs, and too little time on our prospect. The best plan is to make a check list of all tools and supplies and to faithfully carry out an orderly check off prior to leaving on the camping trip.

It may seem that too much space is given to the things which all campers know, or should know. As I mentioned before, a prospector can find gold with a frying pan or even with a shovel blade, and metals can be found without all kinds of elaborate precautions and safety advice. This book is written to provide information which will make any prospecting venture a pleasure and which will result in a great recreational adventure. Great camping adventures rarely come off when leaves must be used for toilet paper, frying pans for gold pans, and store string to hold boots on when the laces have broken several times from neglect.

We should consider our own personal health as a tool. Thus, it would be well for those over-thirty campers to have a good physical examination by their family doctor before attempting any serious or strenuous camping ventures. This is especially true when camping or hiking will be done some distance from the main roads or trails. A family doctor can update an immunization chart with booster tetanus and typhoid shots to make sure that the body is ready to fight infections that could result from nail punctures and rusty metal cuts, bad water, and other potentially dangerous infection problems which could lay a prospector low while up in the isolated hills.

In some areas of the country, trail hikers might come across poisonous snakes, so it is logical when you are in such areas to have along a recently dated snake-bite kit. Read all the instructions in this kit and make a dry run or two before you might meet a snake fang to foot. It might be a little too exciting to have to sit down and read the instructions after the snake has sunk its fangs into your hide. A few other bits of snake advice: first, leave all snakes alone; do not kill them, but allow them to have ample room to escape so that they do not feel endangered enough to attack. Avoid putting your hands or feet down on unknown areas without extreme caution, especially when traveling along rocky ledges or terrain where the snakes are likely to be lying in the sun for warmth. Finally, make sure that the old-fashioned snake-bite remedy is left back home in the cabinet. The booze will not help the bite much, and you're likely to do more damage to yourself from falling down on the rocky trails than any snakebite could do to you.

Spend a few hours before going on the trail re-reading a good, *modern* first-aid manual and preparing a first-aid kit. Personal peace of mind and immediate reaction to emergency problems on the trail will repay those few minutes of preparation at home.

The information necessary for emergencies, health and safety factors, elemental outdoor survival, and other details is contained in the suggested reading list in the appendix. It is not that I am trying to avoid some difficult writing, but rather experience has proven to me that these specialized sources of information are worth far more than a few precautionary lines in a small camper's guide such as this book. Remember, this is a guide to prospecting, not an encyclopedia of striking it rich. If I knew everything about striking it rich, Ari and I would be sharing some exotic Greek island!

How To Use The Gold Prospecting Tools

In order to describe the use of the tools that have been gathered, it is necessary to again describe the likely places for your strike to be found.

Remember, gold is one of the heavier metal elements. Because of its density and weight, the metal just does not drift along with the currents of the stream or river. Placer gold, that which has been reduced to the raw metal by erosion, moves very slowly along the bottom of the flowing water, becoming <u>trapped in crevices or behind rocky</u> <u>outcrops, where the water is slowed by the eddying current.</u> The smaller the particles of gold, the farther downstream from the lode or bed source will the metal be found. Thus, the first color in a pan will indicate generally how near or how far you are from the main supply of ore. As the size increases from flour gold to larger particles, you will likely be working upstream and toward the pocket or lode.

The whole idea of a prospect is to hunt down the main source or vein from which the placer gold in a pan was produced. The pan will be your guide along the watershed, bird-dogging the gold to its hiding place. Work along the stream with the pan until the concentrate runs out of gold or color trace. Always work upstream from the vanish point with your pan to eliminate the possibility of a "freak of nature" skip in the trail. No additional color in your pan for a hundred or so feet is a pretty good indication that the gold trail now leaves the stream.

At this point, begin scouting the area to see if you can locate a likely source for the main gold deposit. Outcrops in the surrounding riverbank walls, upturned trees which have exposed deep soils to the wash waters, small side streams feeding into the main channel, dry gulches can all be the source of the color trace. Then begins the usually tough job of getting soil samples to the river's edge so that you can begin the pan-washing process for "float" gold to check your hunch. I can truthfully say that hauling pails of gravel and soil down steep river banks is not child's play, but hot and difficult work. This is part of the game of prospecting, the exciting part, for hidden nearby is the payoff point of your venture.

All of what has been said so far presumes that you will be prospecting along running watersheds. If by chance the prospect has taken you to arid or dry areas, the problem of panning samples becomes considerably more difficult. In this event, you will have need of stout boxes or sacks in which to carry the samples (numbered in the order in which they have been taken from the dry creek bed) out of the area to a water source for washing. There are some prospectors who can work dry soil, and there are some dry-washing machines, but these machines and skills are usually beyond the talents of the average amateur prospector. The appendix will mention sources for this kind of machinery.

In describing the various tools of our prospecting kit, I mentioned the prospect hammer, chisels (gads), and pry bars. When the trace of color leaves the stream bed, and the working of the sides of the hills begins, you will likely find rock outcrop areas which must be examined for ore pockets. Your hammer, gad, and bars will provide the force and power to dig into and break apart the outcrop in a simple fashion. This kind of mining is very simple, for all that is sought are samples of rock to crush and wash to make the test for float gold. The search is for pockets within the rock that could hold the source of your trace gold. Some of the more serious prospectors carry along, in addition to the tools mentioned in this section, an iron mortar and pestle in which to carry out the final, fine crushing of the rock sample prior to pan-washing. The gad point chisels will be of great benefit in working loose bits of quartz vein from the rock or in gathering whole crystal or gem samples from vugs.

As progress is made in prospecting experience, you might decide upon a number of adaptations to the basic tool kit. You will probably end up with some strange-looking tools which have no name and whose use only you will know, because they were made to solve some problem or other. Those readers who live in the major metropolitan areas should be careful when carrying mining tools in their car. You might be subject to a good deal of embarrassment and fright if you are stopped by the police some night and have this assortment of tools with you. The average prospector's kit looks more like a burglar's jimmy kit than anything else. The ordinary policeman, will understandably, be inclined to have grave doubts about your honesty, especially if there have been a number of recent break-ins in the neighborhood. Avoid this possibility by leaving all of the prospect tools at home with your camping gear, or by spending the winter bragging to all the neighbors about the almost fabulous strike you made on the last trip. This will mark you as some kind of harmless nut, and this brag will supply the evidence you need for the kind but doubtful policeman. I can just imagine the dilemma of some amateur prospector being stopped at midnight at Dearborn and Jackson streets in the heart of the Chicago financial district with a trunk full of chisels, pry bars, and hammers! I would like to be there to hear the explanation that is given to some tired hardnosed cop!

We now come to the use of the gold pan. You have decided upon your first sand bar, pulled the new pan out of the pack, and are ready for the first load of gold. It isn't quite that simple, though. You should have some practice before you fill the pan with supposedly rich gravel. As mentioned earlier, gold is very heavy, and of course this is the secret of your gold pan. The prospector, in a sense, provides a small river current inside the rim of the gold pan and duplicates the washing process of nature. The swirling of the water in the pan and the rocking motion of the hands and wrists duplicate in a small way the natural washing refinement of the river placers. In order to practice before you go out on the trail, make up a small washtub load of gravel for your practice washings. In an old tub thoroughly mix sand, soil, gravel of various sizes, and about a half pound of #6 and #4 lead birdshot or steel B.B.'s. Tumble the mixture in your tub so that it is thoroughly mixed. Lead is heavy—not as heavy as gold, but heavy enough for the birdshot to serve as gold for the practice sessions.

Begin washing the gravel mixture, using another tubful of water for a supply of water and also as a place in which to wash the gravel. To help keep the water clean, put a hose with a gently running stream of water into the washtub. The object of the trial washing is to see how much of the gold (lead shot) can be recovered from the pan. The lead will act much like gold in the pan, since its weight will pull it to the bottom and you will be able to wash away the loose soil.

Now for the actual use of the pan. The first thing to do is to fill the pan to the brim with gravel, and shake it slightly to settle the earth in the pan. Pick out and toss aside the larger pieces of rock of no value, first making sure that all of the clinging soil has been washed from these pieces. Gently rake your fingers through the gravel, pulling the larger rocks to the top; again, wash these and throw them aside. After removing the major amount of rock, place the pan carefully in the water and allow the gentle river currents (stir the water in the washtub with your hand or use a running hose) to wash away the organic soil, twigs, and growth materials. Break up the remaining soil and clay so that the gold can settle to the bottom of the pan.

First step in gold panning: Hand picking the large rocks.

This should leave the pan about half full of small pebbles and sandy material. This residue will be worked out of the pan with the rocking motion of your arms and hands. Holding the pan by opposing rims, with the pan tipped away from the body, the hands and arms begin a slow circular motion. This circular motion is rather like an oval (kind of racetrack-shaped), the idea being to bring the water in the pan into a movement which will create a faster motion at the end of the stroke. Much like race cars on a track, the speed will make the water, which is

Second step: first wetting to let loose earth run from the pan in the stream.

Third step: Raking the gravel with the fingers to loosen the earth in the pan.

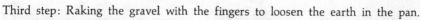

carrying the lighter soil materials, climb the wall of the pan. Since the gold pan is tipped slightly, the water will roll over the rim of the pan on the opposite side, carrying away the excess gravel and soil.

Very soon you will notice the shot particles racing around the bottom of the pan, clinging to the outside bottom of the pan where the side walls begin. This is the effect you are trying to achieve with the washing action. Now begin to exercise a good deal more care in the

Fourth step: Washing the gravel using arm and wrist motion to reduce the gravel to concentrate.

washing action, since the shot (gold), though heavy in comparison to the other soil, will begin to ride up the sides of the pan. To help break up the rising action of the gold and to make a more efficient wash, the pan should be turned in your hand. Thus, there are two motions, the arms and shoulders moving the pan in a long circular movement, and your hands slowly spinning the pan while continuing the larger motion. This sounds awkward, but a few practice sessions with the pan and shot will solve the problem.

Note that in addition to the quantity of shot remaining in the pan, there will be some additional materials. You have now worked the pan down to the concentrate. There are some mineral materials which are plentiful in nature. These materials are quite heavy. As a result of this weight, these materials cannot easily be washed away, leaving just the gold. The increased motion necessary to make these heavy concentrates move over the pan rim will also wash away the fine gold from the pan. The most common materials left in the concentrate will be black magnetite (magnetic iron oxide), pyrites, or fool's gold (yellow iron disulfide), ilmenite (iron titanate), and the gem gravels—ruby, zircon, garnet, and others. These mineral gravels should be carefully checked to make sure that there are no large, good quality gem stones among the concentrate.

Final step: Dry the bits of remaining concentrate and transfer the material to the carrying vial.

At this point in the panning operation, if you are simply seeking color to help follow a trace for the gold deposit, you can see the minute flakes of gold in the pan. A choice can now be made to continue work at this spot or to move along the stream bed seeking a richer trace deposit. If you decide to work the location at which you are, it is best to make a number of partial washes, reducing the pans of gravel to concentrate. Save the concentrate from several pans in a small vial for a final washing at some later time. The same will hold true for the working of a larger or richer deposit. With some experience you will be able to tell just about how good (rich) the gravel is that you are working by the amount of color and by the size of the grains of gold.

To get on with the job of final washing, or working of the total concentrate. Notice that as you swirl the pan, the material in the pan will space itself out, much like cars in a race. The lighter sands will, under the pressure of the moving water, race on ahead of the heavier iron and gold metals. Thus, you will begin to see a real separation occur between the gold and the remaining concentrate. With care it is possible to stop the motion of the pan and remove the excess material with your fingers. This will help to reduce the remaining concentrates without endangering the loss of the gold in the pan.

With practice you will find that your right thumb can be used to trap the gold particles while allowing the black sands to wash past. This black sand, after being thoroughly dried, can be removed from the concentrate with the horseshoe magnet from your field kit. Cover the working ends of the magnet with some folds of paper or foil. The power of the magnet will work through this wrap, so you can proceed to pick up the black sand from the concentrate. When the black sand has been lifted and moved from over the pan, pull off the wrapping from the magnet, and discard the wrap and magnetic sand. This will leave the magnet clean, and the pan free of some of the waste matter in the concentrate.

There may be other materials left in the pan which must be removed by additional careful panning or by the very careful brushing away with the thumb or fingers. The gold and the few impurities that are left are then transferred to a vial by working the gold along with a couple of drops of water from the pan onto a small piece of paper or thin metal foil which has been folded to create a valley-like crease. After the gold has dried, it can be carefully poured into the holding vial. Extreme care should be used toward the end of the panning operation, for it is very easy to tip, spill, or drop the pan or folded transfer sheet and thereby waste the whole effort to reduce the pan of gravel to gain the few specks of gold.

Since the use of the gold pan is the key to success for the amateur prospector, any time spent in practice with the pan will be repaid by its successful use in the field. There are a couple of interesting things to know about gold pans. First of all, you will note that the pan is rough and crude-looking when you receive it from the supplier. Do not make any effort to polish the pan; rather, build a good wood fire and put the pan into the flames. This will "burn out" the pan. A gold pan that has even a speck of oil in it will tend to make the gold float to the top of the water, thus defeating the prospector's best effort to make the gold settle to the bottom of the pan for concentration.

Packing earth, at Carson's.

Veteran prospectors regularly "burn out" their pans to make sure that no grease from their cooking gear has contaminated the precious pan. It is perfectly possible to use any of the modern-day detergents to remove all traces of grease from the gold pan, but using detergents is not nearly so romantic. Prospectors sometimes even dry their concentrate by putting the wet pan directly over the heat of a low campfire. Be careful to use a pliers when handling a hot pan to avoid burned fingers. Earlier I mentioned the rough finish of most gold pans. The inside of the pan should be left rough, for this provides a series of very small riffles, or baffles, which tumble the sand in the pan while providing a kind of holding barrier for the very minute particles of gold.

Now that a few pans of gravel have been worked to get the knack of washing, do not get hung up on the ritual of gold pan manipulation. There are likely as many ways of successfully working a gold pan as there are wet-kneed prospectors on a river. As long as you can make the gold pan work and not lose the gold dust, you have solved the basic mechanics of gold-getting. Do your own thing, but do it very carefully. A hurried washing of a pan of gravel could result in some faulty evidence and a wasted prospecting journey. A careless working of the pan might cause a misjudgment of the color trace, and lead to making a wrong decision that there is no gold in the prospect area.

The above should be enough to keep you from using a good gold pan as a cooking pot. Use an old tin can for a cooking pot if necessary, or go hungry, but don't use the gold pan as a kettle! I recall meeting a young couple doing some panning along the Yuba River. The girl was very proudly and efficiently heating their noon time meal in the gold pan! It made me shudder to see that greasy noodle soup bubbling in that pan! She mentioned to me in passing that she had not had too much luck during the morning using that pan, so she had decided to stop panning and cook their lunch! As I passed her husband who was working his pan along the bank of the river, I offered him the hint about the grease-free gold pan being the best. I hope that their later prospects worked better for them!

As you read other books on mining and prospecting— and I suggest that you read all you can find—you will see that there are several other suggested ways of getting the gold reduced to the concentrated form. I will add a cautionary note at this juncture concerning the separation of the gold from the concentrate by using mercury. Mercury, a heavy, liquid, metallic element, sometimes called quicksilver, mixes quickly with gold and silver to form a chemical mixture called an "amalgam." This amalgam of mercury with other metals is called an "alloy," and can be useful to skilled miners.

Since mercury is poisonous and can be easily mishandled by unknowing persons, the beginning prospector is best advised to skip the methods of getting his gold cleaned, or rectified, by using mercury. Perhaps after more experience, or after watching someone use the mercury, the reader might like to try this method of freeing his gold from the concentrate. I do point out that this method of refining is, or could be, very dangerous, and should be used with extreme caution. The reason that I dislike using the mercury method is the fear of contaminating my camping kit and food-preparation gear. I also fear the contamination of my body from accidentally getting mercury into my mouth from my fingers, or from rubbing this dangerous liquid into my eyes. The specks of gold in my pan are not worth the risk to my health.

There are various other portable mining devices that may be of some value to the amateur prospector. I don't use such tools, simply because they require some kind of additional packing help. I dislike using pack animals or expensive four-wheel jeeps to haul prospecting equipment. The average camper-prospector is not a professional and really has little need for such tools. For those who might be interested in sluice boxes, trommels, concentrators, and the like, the suppliers listed in the appendix will have these tools listed in their catalogs. For those readers who might be skin-divers and who would like to prospect under water, there are several relatively small, portable, floating power dredges. These dredges work much like a home vacuum cleaner, and are powered by a small gasoline motor. The whole dredge machine floats on a substantial, rubber, raft-like affair. These tools are good for those who like to dive and who wish to work in deep waters beyond the depth at which a pan miner can work.

I seem to be closing all sections with some kind of cautionary note to the prospector. I will have to do the same here, for there are some rather serious restrictions concerning gold. Our government dislikes the idea of citizens having gold bullion in their possession. This stems from the government's desire to protect its investment in gold as a monetary standard. The government is also interested in knowing which of its citizens are amassing some unreported wealth. Gold has always been, and in spite of U.S. Government policy, will likely continue to be a popular medium of international exchange. There are some folks who like to keep a few pounds of gold on hand in the event of a major disaster to our national economy. Gold, like diamonds, provides an easily exchanged form of international currency. There are some poor souls who so fear disaster that they are only comfortable with their small horde of bullion.

If you find gold you may keep it, but only in the raw state in which you found the metal. Do not attempt to refine the gold or to melt it into bars, or ingots. This will result in a great deal of trouble from Uncle Sam. You can sell the gold through licensed gold buyers who are authorized to deal in raw metals, or through the Treasury Department or to friends, but only in the raw state. Do the right thing and save yourself a great deal of trouble.

Cradle rocking, on the Stanislaus.

Electronic Metal Detectors
and Treasure Finders

The metal detector is a relatively new tool for the prospector. It is the result of the need for mine detectors during wartime and of the modernization of electronic circuitry. These technological advances have led to the development of very small, lightweight machines that can be easily carried and used by young and old. The most simple of these devices operate on the beat-frequency oscillator principle. The BFO principle means that there are two oscillators which feed signals under operator control at two different frequencies into a receiver. The receiver, in turn, tunes the difference between the two frequency beats into an amplifier, which produces a single, low-frequency, steady sound. When this low-frequency signal changes from its *putt-putt* or "motor boating" tone, it means that some metal has interrupted the beat signal. This changes the low, slow audible signal to a higher pitch or squeal. With the change in the beat tone, the prospector knows he has located some metallic material. The time has come for him to probe for the metal that is causing the change in the frequency sound. All too often in my experience the hidden metal turns out to be the universally present beer cap or cigarette wrapper.

There are two other types of metal finders, but the good ones are usually beyond the pocketbook of the average camper. One operates on the null, or induction balance, system, which has receiver coils (see above) that cancel out the signal unless the detector loop is passed over some metallic object. The metallic object upsets the balance of the induction coil and an audible signal is transmitted, alerting the prospector that he has located some hidden metal. The second detector is a reflector type, or penetration detector, in that it is designed to ignore small metallic objects—coins, beer caps, small car parts, and the like, which are near the surface—and to reflect signals from broader masses of metallic material which lie deeper under the ground. This detector is built so that it does not transmit frequency signals to its receiver directly, but only receives signals which are reflected back to the receiver from a metallic source.

The penetration detector might be of use to the prospector, depending on the limitations of his pocketbook. The induction balance system will work quite well on small metallic objects near the surface (6 inches to 5 or 6 feet) of the ground. It has the added advantage over the BFO of being able to detect metal at a much deeper level. The cost of the induction balanced detector can vary from eighty to several hundred dollars. The manufacturers of these machines can usually supply, on order, a water-proofed model for use in skin-diving or for searching under the water along the edges of lakes and streams.

The use of an electronic metal locator requires some degree of skill on the part of the operator. This can only be obtained by following the manufacturer's instructions to the letter and putting in a good deal of practice. Since this is not "lead shot" practice but the real thing, practice to your heart's content at some nearby beach or recreational area. It could be that during the practice session you will uncover a considerable amount of lost coinage.

The use of the detector requires a consistent pattern of operation. The loop, or head of the finder, must be kept at a constant height above the ground, usually about two inches. As the operator swings the detector loop from side to side, the wand to which the loop is fastened tends to make an arc of from two inches to five or six inches above the ground at the end of the swing. Thus, it is the attention of the operator to his chore which corrects for the swing and keeps the loop on a constant productive level.

With practice, the treasure hunter or prospector will learn to read the signals coming from his sound speaker or earphones. He will begin to "read" beer caps and package foils and learn to ignore their signals.

He will also learn to make the proper settings on his meter which will "read" precious metals in a manner different from that of baser metals, such as iron and tin. With practice and experience, his average of success will increase, and his percentage of recovery will zoom dramatically.

Make no mistake, these are serious tools. However, there is a kind of exciting avarice which overtakes the operator. It is the excitement that comes from the anticipation of getting something for nothing, and that something could turn out to be a small fortune.

Unless you are seeking unusual items, you should use your locator in places where people have lived in the past or are living now. The kinds of treasure we all seek are coins, rings, old firearms, relics from military campaigns and Indian wars, and, of course, gold and silver hidden inside the mother rocks and placers. In the main, it can be said that what will be worth finding will have been lost or hidden by someone in the past. Many a treasure is lying hidden, put there on purpose by someone who distrusted banks or who could not get to a bank to put the money away for safekeeping. In the past, also, many of the highway-men would cache their loot while on the run from pursuers. Their intent was to return and claim the cache at a later date, but death on the trail or in prison thwarted their plan. It is also very likely that in their hurry to avoid capture, the bandits made a poor location map of their treasure spot. After a few years had passed and some of the surrounding areas were settled, the face of the land changed. The robbers just couldn't find the cache and recover their loot.

When you take your detector from the car, you must begin to think as did the people who lived in the area which you will search. Common hiding places for small hordes of coins, gold, and jewelry are alongside fenceposts near old houses, at the corners of old foundations, in the hollow crotches of trees, in side walls, and above the doorways in old houses. A favorite hiding place for handguns was over the top of the door to the bedroom or over the header of the front door.

There have been too many recorded treasure finds to ignore the metal detector or pass it off as a toy. The various club newspapers, manufacturer's news notes, books, and personal experiences have told of genuine treasure finds both large and small. It is true that most of the finds have been in the small coin and ring category, which might amount to some two hundred dollars. I can safely say that the sheer fun of getting out of doors with a detector and searching for treasure is worth the cost of the machine.

As you begin using a metal detector, learn good operating habits to go along with the manufacturer's instructions. First, visualize the detector at work. The frequency beat is sent out in a fixed direction. Using a six inch loop, usually these two signals are fixed to intersect at a point ten to thirteen inches below the loop. Thus, the operator is directing a cone-shaped signal into the ground. To get a consistent reading, the signal should always be directed toward the same depth. Consistently holding the detector two inches from the ground and not allowing the loop to tip to the side will give the best and most reliable reading from the detector. It should not seem necessary to tell you to check the battery power before using the machine and to have an extra set of batteries along out on a trail, but all too many metal detectors are found to be dead weight because of battery failure. Metal detectors work much better in areas which enjoy good rainfall or heavy morning dew. It is a catchword among metal detector hobbyists that wet beaches are better than dry ones, and that wet, dewy, or post-rain mornings are better than dry sunny afternoons for getting good signals from the earth. The reason for this effect is that electric signals are conducted much more easily through wet or moist ground than through dry, hard, packed soil.

Look for the unexpected when you hear the beat signal change. The unexpected is the potential payoff for the treasure hunter. Also, do not expect that items which have been hidden in the earth for many years will look the same as they did when buried. Iron rusts, and gold, silver, copper—in fact, most metals—tarnish and begin to form salts with the surrounding materials in the earth. The treasure hunter will find silver coins which seem to be old black iron buttons; copper coins or jewelry which looks as if it were made of some sickly green moon metal; and gold coins, or dust, from which the poke bag has rotted, leaving a lumpish black mass that looks like some bug's nest. Most people would walk by these finds because they look unappealing. Don't let this happen! Let your imagination, your eyes and hands examine all detector signal finds with great care. Unless you are using the metal detector on picnic beaches on a Monday morning to find the weekend's lost coins, you will not likely see fresh, new, shiny coins or rings.

I remember well the man who introduced me to metal detectors. When I was told about him by a friend, I'm sure that I had the amused smile most doubtful Thomases display when told some outrageous tale. Just a few minutes at my new friend's house, viewing his two huge milk pails full of college class rings, coins, and other metal objects, plus a demonstration in his yard of the machine at work, made me a convert. This man owns a most beautiful golden Inca ring which was washed upon a beach in Florida and which signalled his detector through the sands one morning after a harsh Atlantic storm had lashed the beach. Most likely this Inca ring was from the hand of an ancient Spanish sailor lost overboard at sea or drowned in the wreck of a galleon smashed by hurricane winds.

The metal detector has operational use for amateur prospectors other than that of providing treasure-hunting fun. It can be used, in the hands of an experienced operator, to locate prospect holes along riverbanks, in dry gulches, in pockets in rock formations, etc. Since the BFO and induction balance detectors are usually light in weight, they can be carried along the trails in a kit bag. The detectors, by their very design, are a bit awkward; however, most of them can be dismantled for packing. I find that the detector is especially helpful in following color trace after it has left the river waters. The machine should be considered as an auxillary tool to help locate the path to the gold source. The prospector must, by experience or trial and error, make the judgment as to where the deposit of gold lies. With this decision made, he can turn to the detector for assistance in sniffing for the pockets of ore hidden from sight in the gravel or rocks.

The appendix on page 60 gives the names of the manufacturers who are best known together with some of their better prospecting models with prices. If you are interested in this type of equipment, I would suggest that you write to these suppliers for catalogs and make a careful comparative analysis in the light of your needs. All the companies noted in the appendix are reputable firms and manufacture dependable equipment. I might also note here that most of the manufacturing firms can make minor adjustments and special calibrations if they are told that the machine will be used for special purposes, such as gold detection. This specialization might put some limitations on the use of the detector for general treasure hunting.

I will close this section with my usual caveats. The treasure-hunting field is especially subject to the private property laws. The laws from state to state vary, but normally on public lands and in abandoned areas, the finder is the keeper (except for the state's usual share of all treasure trove and the IRS's interest in your increased wealth). Check the local treasure trove laws to make sure that you will be the owner before wasting time finding something valuable. It would be heart-breaking to hit a real treasure trove only to find that you are not the owner of the newly found loot, since the state or another individual by prior right has taken the booty. The state of Texas is notorious for confiscation of treasure, especially Spanish treasure, which sometimes is valuable enough to make some state officials lick their chops.

Remember the advice concerning private property—stay off unless permission has been secured to hunt for buried treasure. In most cases, if you feel you have good evidence, from research, of hidden treasure on private land, it is possible to negotiate permission to work the site. Do not tell anyone any details of your research, even after making a written agreement with a property owner. If you do reveal details of your treasure, you may find that you have to post a 'round-the-clock watch to protect the site! Most people, however, are fascinated with the idea of finding a treasure on their land and will cooperate whole-heartedly. They will, of course, expect to share in the find, and rightly so. Most working agreements can be negotiated at from ten to twenty-five percent share of the treasure going to the property owner and the balance to the finder, who has borne all search expenses.

Something of a warning, but something that will be learned very quickly if you do not heed the warning, is that silence is the order of the day in the treasure-finding business. You may love your wife or girl friend very much, but they too come under the class of suspicious characters when you are after a real dandy of a treasure. To change an old World War II phrase for our purposes: *Wagging tongues sink treasure seekers!*

The Practical Aspects of Staking
and Filing A Claim

Possibly nowhere on earth is there such a set of complicated laws and regulations as those found in the general body of the United States mining law. In the early days of mining, prior to the national mining laws enacted by Congress in 1872, the mining regulations were decided upon in each mining district. That is, the mining district area having been decided upon, the miners who were engaged in prospecting within the district voted in democratic fashion to follow a certain set of rules within the district. Since many of the miners moved from district to district, and since most of their regulations were based on common sense and common need, these district mining regulations became, in effect, the law.

On May 10, 1872, the good men of Congress, under the urging of lawyers in need of legal fees and of large mine operators in need of protection for their investments, passed the Federal Mining Law. The good congressmen, in their usual fashion of acting in semi-ignorance of facts, assumed that since a vein of rock disappeared into the ground, it must continue in such fashion straight down to the very bowels of the earth. Thus, simply put, that august body, the Congress, declared that this was the case and that the law should so declare it to be.

This left the prospector and miner with the real problem of staking his claim in relation to the reality of the land upon which he stood. The ore vein which he had discovered, because of the folding and faulting of the country rock, may have had an acute angle of dip ("dip" is the degree of angle in a compass direction which the vein has in relationship to the surface of the earth at that point) which could take the best part of the discovery beyond the limits of his claim stake area. So too, the

This drawing shows two rock strata (A;B) and a dike (C) which have not eroded as much as the surrounding country rock. Since the direction of the ridge is north, the *strike* is north. The *dip* is westerly for A, and B, and easterly for C.

prospector had to determine, or guess, the direction of the vein in relation to the surface so that he might stake out the most advantageous claim. The direction of the vein is called the "strike" (or the compass direction which the vein follows in relation to the surface of the earth).

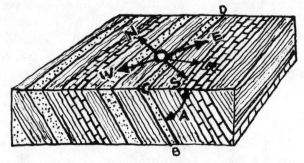

To determine the *strike* and *dip* of inclined strata rock, place the compass on the edge of the bed plane (BCD), the arrow at right angles to the strike (R) indicates the direction of the dip. The strike direction (NOD) and dip direction (SOR) are read on the compass. The angle of dip (A) is read with the clinometer.

The federal law of 1872 said that the prospector or miner staking a lode claim could have the right to a claim not over 1500 feet long and not over 600 feet wide. The only other dimensional limitation in this law was that the two ends of the claim had to be parallel to each other. Since the lawmakers did not specify that the side lines of the claim had to be at right angles to the parallel ends, the claim in fact could take any shape, as long as the ends were parallel, and it was not over 1500 feet in length, and the side line was not over 300 feet from the center of the lode or vein. It is easy to see why the men at law waxed fat, while the miners turned to violence to defend their "rights."

A placer claim, since it is a surface claim, may contain not more than twenty acres for each claimant. However, up to eight claimants may band together to stake a continuous claim for some 160 acres of surface placer holding. Since the law requires that a claim must produce some discovery of value, and that each claim must be worked or improved each year to the extent of one hundred dollars in assessment value, it is an advantage to stake the larger joint claim, since the one discovery and the one assessment will cover the entire claim as one unit. These same work rules apply to the lode claim, though the extent of landholdings vary slightly. The smallest legal mining parcel of land is ten acres.

In any event, the common law of the miners, combined with the law of the land and supplemented by various state laws and regulations, made for a very, very complicated body of rules. About the only thing that I can do here is to give a general description of the method of land survey in the United States and to provide guides to the further detailed location of information pertaining to filing claims.

The early days of our country found the legal and political divisions being established in a rather helter-skelter fashion. Within the regulations of the Northwest Ordinance (1787), provisions were made to survey and establish all legal and political divisions on a standard measurement system. This standard is based upon a system of townships which are one mile square and which are then divided up into thirty-six sections, beginning with the northeast section as number one, continuing from east to west, with the tiers of sections reckoned from north to south. Each township is given a number and compass direction line called the principle meridian, with a second reference to a line called a base line, from which reference is made to a range number and compass direction. The township numbers read north and south, and the range numbers read east and west from the origin lines. A reference to the accompanying maps will give the reader an idea of how the legal description of land and its subdivision are arrived at by the civil authorities.

It is extremely important that the prospector, in staking and filing his claim, record proper measurements and locations in relationship to the federal survey for legal subdivisions. Most of the land of interest to the amateur prospector will be in the Western states, and it is in these states that much of the public land exists. There are some public lands, mainly national forest lands, open to the prospector in the Middle and Eastern states, but the prospector must secure permission to prospect from the proper management official. I have appended a list of the state offices at which a prospector may inquire concerning prospecting rights, permissions, and mining regulations.

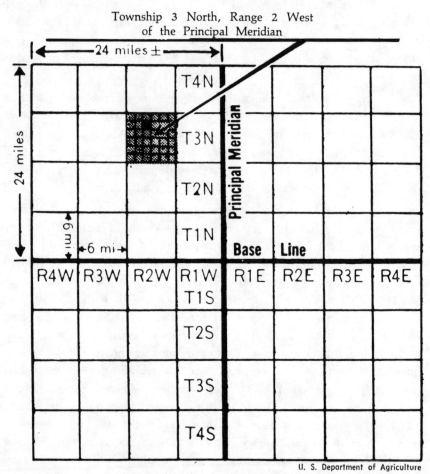

Township 3 North, Range 2 West
of the Principal Meridian

U. S. Department of Agriculture

Dividing an area into townships.

Section 9. Township 3 North, Range 2 West of
the Principal Meridian

6	5	4	3	2	1
7	8	9	10	11	12
18	17	16	15	14	13
19	20	21	22	23	24
30	29	28	27	26	25
31	32	33	34	35	36

Sections 1 through 6 on the north side and 7, 18, 19, 30,
and 31 on the west side are fractional sections.

U. S. Department of Agriculture

A township divided into sections.

Section—1 Sq. Mile—640 Acres

U. S. Department of Agriculture

Section of land showing acreage and distances.

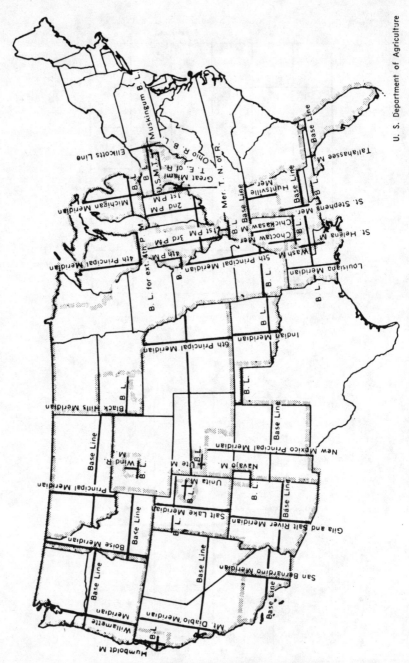

Location of the several prime meridians and their base lines.

U. S. Department of Agriculture

At the present time, an amateur prospector may experience some difficulty in securing permission to enter government lands. Recently some rather dishonest people have used the guise of a prospector to make claim rights on some rather handsome vacation lands. They have done this claim filing legally, fulfilling the requirements for claim and patent, and ended up owning choice property within the limits of public domain lands. The federal government is taking steps to make sure that this misuse of the mining laws is stopped (See: Congressional Act of July 23, 1955). Thus, the amateur prospector who does make a strike must be doubly careful to fulfill all of the requirements of the law and to establish the fact that he is interested in mineral development, and not a beautiful cabin site or a cheap source for commercial sand, gravel, or clay supplies!

Since the staking and filing of a mine claim is so complicated, it is essential that the prospector be given proper guidance. This is beyond the scope of this book. However, by referring to the appendix, you will find sources of detailed information relative to the field work necessary, and the documentation required to protect a claim in the event of a discovery.

Go out and enjoy being an amateur prospector. Be as familiar as possible with the federal and local laws pertaining to mining rights. Check to make sure that the land can be claimed if a discovery is made, and proceed with the prospect. Prudent use of all tools and camping gear, and the proper maintenance of physical stamina will assure a most happy and enjoyable vacation.

The appendices of this book are the most important part of the volume. I have always had difficulty finding the complete details of some information I needed. It was long hours of work trying to locate all of the addresses of suppliers, government offices, and specialized equipment. When I had finally gathered this material, I wanted to put it down for you and for all campers to use to make their vacations more fun.

Go, man! Go find a bonanza, if not of gold, then of fun with your family or friends in places where the average tourist is seldom seen.

Just remember these points:

There is plenty of gold left in the earth. The reserve of the United States is in the hundreds of millions of dollars.

Gold can occur any place, and it will be any place you look. It might not be enough to excite you, but it's there. Find it.

The modern camper-prospector stands a much better chance to make a strike than did the bearded, flea-bitten '49er. These men did not have the reference books, the good maps, the histories of claims, strikes, and mines to give them leads to find new prospect holes. The oldtimers did not have a fast car and camper to make their trip a pleasure, good roads to get them to the prospect, nor fancy modern scientific tools to give some help to blind chance.

Remember, even today, amidst all the sophisticated mining tools, the professional prospector still relies on the old iron gold pan to make a final check on his modern geologic theories and tests. Your pan, magnet, magnifying glass, and other tools, and a few trips to give you experience will put you on an equal footing with the best of the pros.

All of the gold and silver discoveries that have produced the billions of dollars in bullion about which we talked in the beginning of this book were made by someone just like you. They were walking the hills and along the rivers, testing with their pan, following leads, and finally striking a glory hole. You can do the same, for Lady Luck holds no favorites, either in time or in place.

Good luck! My best wishes go with you. I hope that the water is not too cold, the trail not too rocky and rough, and that the color in your pan is bright and plentiful. Have a good trip and return safely.

Our camp on the Stanislaus.

List of Regional Offices of U. S. Department of Interior, Bureau of Land Management.

List of Federal agencies which will advise on prospecting lands within its jurisdiction: when applying for information concerning specific land areas open for prospecting, furnish, as nearly as possible, a complete legal description of the land. Note that although state and miner law cannot supercede federal mining laws, these local laws can further limit the actions of prospectors. Therefore, check carefully with both the federal and state people prior to conducting any serious prospecting. The Bureau of Land Management regional offices are located at:

630 Sansome St., San Francisco, California 94111

1245 North 29th St., Billings, Montana 59101

1015 W. Tijeras Avenue N.W., Albuquerque, New Mexico 87101

1 Swan Island Station, Portland, Oregon 97218

238 Federal Building, Salt Lake City, Utah 84101

These regional offices will give you the name and address of the person to contact in the Bureau's land offices in various cities. It should also be noted here that certain lands, i.e., Indian reservations, national forests, etc., are managed by other offices than those of the Bureau of Land Management. However, the regional Bureau offices listed will refer you to the proper official.

The responsibility for the land management in each state varies from state to state. This responsibility also changes departmental hands from time to time. The best advice I can give you is to write to the department of land management of the state in which you would like to prospect. Address the letter to the department at the state capitol building, in the capitol city. This letter will reach the proper official, and you will obtain the needed information. In my experience, the wheels of government move slowly so allow yourself plenty of time to carry out your correspondence before you leave on your trip. There is no way I know of, outside of enlisting the help of a friendly legislator, to get any official department of any government body to move in any unseemly haste!

APPENDIX II: A.

GENERAL GUIDE
TO METAL DETECTORS

MANUFACTURER	MODEL	TYPE	USE	INDICATOR	PRICE
Dectron, Inc. Box 243 San Gabriel, Ca. 91778	*Model 711T	Induction Balance	General Purpose	Speaker, earphone	149.00 ✦ 6.00
	*Model 7-T	Induction Balance	General Purpose	Speaker	139.50
D-Tex Electronics Co. Box 451 Garland, Texas 75040	Koin-King	BFO	General Purpose	Earphone	$136.95
	DeLux	BFO	General Purpose	Speaker, meter earphone	189.75
	Professional	BFO	General Purpose	Speaker, meter earphone	252.45
Fisher Detector Co. Box 640 Palo Alto, Calif. 94303	Orion Model 121	Induction Balance	General Purpose	Speaker, earphone	129.50
	*Metalert Model 70	Induction Balance	General Purpose	Plug in speaker, meter, earphone	158.50 ✦17.50
	*Gemini	Transmitter Receiver	Heavy Duty	Speaker, meter earphone	189.50 ✦ 7.50

*Machine Will Detect Magnetic Minerals Such as Iron and Steel and also Non-magnetic metals, gold, etc.
✦Indicates Additional Cost for Headphone Set.

MANUFACTURER	MODEL	TYPE	USE	INDICATOR	PRICE
Gardner Electronics Co. 4729 N. 7th Ave. Phoenix, Arizona 85013	*Model 165	Transmitter Receiver	Heavy Duty	Meter, earphone	195.00
	*Model 190	BFO	General Purpose	Speaker, meter earphone	210.00
	Model 191A	BFO	General Purpose	Speaker, meter earphone	295.00
	*Model 180	BFO	General Purpose	Speaker earphone	315.00
Garrett Electronics Co. Box 28666 Dallas, Texas 77340	*Playmate	BFO	General Purpose	Speaker, meter earphone	119.95
	Sidewinder	BFO	General Purpose	Speaker, meter earphone	139.95
	Provider	BFO	General Purpose	Speaker, meter earphone	199.50
	Hunter	BFO	General Purpose	Speaker, meter earphone	229.50
Goldak Co. 1101 N. Air Way Glendale, Ca. 91201	Commander Jr. Model *820	Induction Balance	General Purpose	Speaker, earphone	119.50
	Commander *Model 720	Induction Balance	General Purpose	Speaker, meter earphone	149.50
	Bonanza Model 1100	Transmitter Receiver	Heavy Duty	Speaker, meter earphone	175.00
Heath Instrument Co. Benton Harbor, Michigan 48022	Heath Kit CD-48	Induction Balance	General Purpose	Speaker, meter	$69.95
Jetco Electronic Co. Box 132 Huntsville, Tex. 77018	*Search-master 550	BFO	General Purpose	Speaker	89.50
	*Huntmaster 770	BFO	General Purpose	Speaker, meter	129.50
	*Treasure Hawk 990	BFO	General Purpose	Speaker, meter	189.50
White Electronics Co. 1011 Pleasant Valley Road, Sweet Home, Ore. 97386	*Coinmaster 3TR	Induction Balance	General Purpose	Meter, speaker earphone	169.50
	*Coinmaster 4TR	Induction Balance	General Purpose	Meter, speaker earphone	199.50
	*Goldmaster	Induction Balance	General Purpose	Meter, speaker earphone	269.50
	Treasure-master 80TR	Induction Balance	General Purpose	Meter, speaker earphone	395.00

*Machine Will Detect Magnetic Minerals Such as Iron and Steel, and also Non-magnetic metals, gold, etc.

APPENDIX II: B

MINING AND PROSPECTING TOOLS

Many of the reference books given in Appendix IV will lead you to a source of supplies for all types of prospecting equipment, amateur and heavy commercial. A good general information source for all types of tools and equipment is *MacRae's Blue Book*, 78th ed., 1971, a trade directory published by MacRae's Blue Book Company, 100 Shore Drive, Hinsdale, Ill., 60521, and which should be available in most good sized libraries. *Sweets Catalog* can usually be found in libraries. The telephone book "yellow pages" for large cities will usually provide a lead which can be used to locate a manufacturer for information. Do not expect large manufacturers to sell to individuals. These concerns will give you the names of dealers who can supply your needs.

The following suppliers and manufacturers will furnish you with information or catalogs. There is a small charge in some cases, refundable with your first purchase.

A. ASSAYERS - GOLD BUYERS - SMELTERS

1. Colorado Assaying Company
   2013 Welton St.
   Denver, Colorado 80201

2. Eastern Smelting and Refining Corp.
   32 Bubier St.
   Lynn, Mass. 01903

3. Laucks Testing Laboratories
   1008 Western Ave.
   Seattle, Wa. 98104

4. Northwest Testing Laboratories
   2nd and James St.
   Seattle, Washington 98101

5. There are many such assaying firms—Consult the "yellow pages" of telephone directories of all large cities.

B. GOLD PANS AND SMALL TOOLS SUPPLIERS

1. William Ainsworth, Inc.   (Brunton Pocket Transit)
   5151 So. Syracuse St.   (Brunton Compass)
   Englewood, Colo. 80110

2. Alpha Hardware Company   (Gold prospecting tools)
   Main Street
   Nevada City, Calif. 95959

3. The American Gem and Mineral Supplier Association
   P. O. Box 274,
   Costa Mesa, California 92626

4. Exanimo Electronic Co.   (Gold prospecting supplies)
   Segundo, Colo. 81070   (Detectors)

5. Gibralter Equipment and Manufacturing Co.
   P. O. Box 304   (General tools—small & large)
   Alton, Ill. 62002

6. Gold Bug   (Gold prospecting tools and detectors)
   Box 588
   Alamo, Calif. 94507

7. Kitco Company
   P. O. Box 112,   (Excellent small patented
   Hackensack, N. J. 07601   rock-crusher-morter)

8. Miner's Exchange
   Box 64   (Gold prospector's supplies)
   Nampa, Idaho 83651

9. Miner's and Prospector's Supplies
   177 Main St.   (Gold prospector's supplies)
   Newcastle, Calif. 95658

10. National Treasure Hunter's League
    Box 53   (Gold pans and detectors)
    Mesquite, Texas 75149

11. Rusha Instrument Company
    6123 Hillcroft Avenue   (Superdip Compass)
    Houston, Texas 77001

C. HEAVY MINING EQUIPMENT SUPPLIERS (Portable Dredges, trommels, separators sluice boxes, etc.)

1. The Deister Concentrator Co., Inc.
   Glasgow and Wayne Streets   (Washing and Separator
   Fort Wayne, Indiana 46801   Equipment)

2. Denver Equipment Division
   Joy Manufacturing Company   (All kinds of placer and
   600 Broadway   lode mining equipment)
   Denver, Colorado 80201

3. Miner's Foundry and Manufacturing Co.
   Nevada City, Calif. 95959

4. New York Engineering Co.
   Babcock Place   (Placer mining equipment)
   Yonkers, N. Y. 10701

5. Parkersburg Die and Tool Co.
   3502 Murdock Ave.   (Placer mining equipment)
   Parkersburg, W. Va. 26101

Washing with the long tom, near Murphy's.

APPENDIX III

A PARTIAL LIST OF OUTSTANDING MINING PROPERTIES DEVELOPED IN THE UNITED STATES

This list of mine properties was chosen because of location, earnings, or unusual names. The list will provide the prospector with a cross-section of the various states, areas, and districts, from which a selection can be made for the planning of a prospecting-camping trip.

Please note that all of these workings are lode mines, and do not reflect the equally rich placer diggings which were associated with these mine areas. The camper-prospector will do well to consider exploring the streams, creeks, and rivers in these mining districts for their traces of color. The method of using this list is to pinpoint some area of interest and take the named mine as a starting point to do research on the area. You will find information in history books, from historical societies, from the study of old maps, from current U.S. charts, and from on-the-site questioning of local residents. Usually the local Chamber of Commerce or booster clubs have little real knowledge of the history of their area. You will pick up bits of information, hints, and the like from conversations with these people which can then be researched. The better prepared you are with the factual information about the area in which you will prospect, the more likely will be your chance of success.

The earnings of these mine properties are based upon a combination of the pre-1934 gold price of $20.67 an ounce, and the former federal fixed price of $35.00 an ounce.

EXAMPLES OF SOME OF THE BETTER MINES IN THE VARIOUS STATES OF THE UNITED STATES — RANDOM SAMPLES

STATE	DISTRICT	COUNTY	MINE NAME	VALUE IN $
Alabama	Hog Mountain	Tallapoosa	Hog Mountain	$250,000
Arizona	Banner	Gilas	Christmas	650,000
Arizona	Vulture	Maricopa	Vulture	1,839,375
Arizona	Black Rock	Yavapai	Gold Bar	195,000
Arizona	Rich Hill	Yavapai	Octave	1,900,000
Arizona	Fortuna	Yerma	Fortuna	3,076,250

STATE	DISTRICT	COUNTY	MINE NAME	VALUE IN $
California	Mother Lode	Amador	Argonaut	25,179,000
California	Wild Rose	Inyo	Skidoo	1,500,000
California	Grass Valley	Nevada	Empire)	315,000,000
California		Nevada	North Star)	
California	Iowa Hill	Placer	Jenny Lind	10,000,000
California	Harrison Gulch	Shasta	Midas	3,563,587
California	Whiskeytown	Shasta	Mad Mule	1,365,000
California	Pocket Belt	Tuolumne	Bonanza	300,000 (in one week)
Colorado	Creede	Mineral	Last Chance	3,730,000
Colorado	Red Mountain	Ouray	Camp Bird	21,884,894
Colorado	Eureka	Animas	Gold King	12,500,000
Colorado	Mt. Wilson	San Miguel	Silver Pick	620,000
Colorado	Telluride	San Miguel	Liberty Bell	15,825,525
Colorado	Cripple Creek Mining Camp	Teller	Portland) Independence) Granite) Strong) Golden Cycle) Vindicator)	477,521,675
Georgia	No District	Cherokee	Creighton	1,212,500
Idaho	Camas	Blaine	Camas #2	1,500,000
Idaho	Quartzburg	Boise	Gold Hill	10,000,000
Idaho	Lion Creek	Custer	Lost Packer	600,000
Idaho	Yankee Fork	Custer	General Custer	8,000,000
Idaho	West View	Gem	Red Warrior	1,000,000
Idaho	Elk City	Idaho	Buster	1,000,000
Idaho	Yellow Jacket	Lemhi	Yellow Jacket	450,000
Idaho	Silver City	Owyhee	Black Jack) DeLamar)	23,000,000
Michigan	No District	Marquette	Ropes	605,000
Montana	Argenta	Beaverhead	Argenta	1,633,750
Montana	Georgetown	Deer Lodge	Southern Cross	600,000
Montana	North Moccasin	Fergus	North Moccasin	10,625,000
Montana	Warm Springs	Fergus	Maiden-Gilt Edge	939,230
Montana	Boulder Creek	Granite	Royal	1,209,475
Montana	Whitehall	Jefferson	Golden Sunlight	1,796,250
Montana	Silver Creek	Lewis & Clark	Drumlummon	9,000,000
Montana	Seven Mile	Lewis & Clark	Scratch Gravel	12,625,000
Montana	Virginia Creek	Lewis & Clark	Jay Gould	5,400,000
Montana	Renova	Madison	Mayflower	1,282,052
Montana	Alder Gulch	Madison	Oro Cache	500,000
Nevada	Wonder	Churchill	Wonder	1,847,250
Nevada	Searchlight	Clark	Quartette	2,800,000
Nevada	Gold Circle	Elko	Elko Prince	2,744,125
Nevada	Goldfield	Esmeralda	Mohawk	104,870,000

STATE	DISTRICT	COUNTY	MINE NAME	VALUE IN $
Nevada	Eureka	Eureka	Eureka	30,750,000
Nevada	Potosi	Humboldt	Getchell	12,142,500
Nevada	Bullfrog	Nye	Shoshone	3,010,025
Nevada	Seven Troughs	Pershing	Mazuma Hills	4,004,500
Nevada	Comstock Lode	Storey	Comstock	214,000,000
New Mexico	Baldy	Colfax	Aztec	2,775,000
New Mexico	Lordsburg	Hidalgo	Emerald	4,750,000
New Mexico	White Oaks	Lincoln	Old Abe	2,500,000
New Mexico	Willow Creek	San Miguel	Pecos	4,457,500
North Carolina	No District	Burke	Mills	1,250,000
North Carolina	No District	Gaston	Kings Mountain	750,000
North Carolina	No District	Montgomery	Iola	900,000
North Carolina	No District	Montgomery	Russell	300,000
North Carolina	No District	Randolph	Hoover Hill	350,000
North Carolina	Gold Hill	Rown	Randolph) Old Field) Honeycutt) Union Copper) Whitney)	4,000,000
Oregon	Connor Creek	Baker	Connor Creek	2,250,000
Oregon	Cracker Creek	Baker	North Pole	9,000,000
Oregon	Mormon Basin	Baker	Rainbow	1,000,000
Oregon	Virtue	Baker	Virtue	2,200,0000
Oregon	Ashland	Jackson	Ashland	1,300,000
Oregon	Upper Applegate	Jackson	Steamboat	350,000
Pennsylvania	No District	Lebanon	Cornwall	937,475
South Carolina	No District	Lancaster	Haile	6,952,000
South Carolina	No District	McCormick	Dorn	900,000
South Dakota	Lead	Lawrence	Homestake	611,250,000
			Largest mine in U.S. and still working)	
South Dakota	Deadwood	Lawrence	Cloverleaf	1,097,125
South Dakota	Garden	Lawrence	Maitland	3,425,000
South Dakota	Hill City	Pennington	Holy Terror	1,900,000
Tennessee	No District	Polk	Ducktown	369,210
Utah	Gold Mountain	Piute	Annie Laurie	3,975,000
Utah	American Fork	Utah	Miller	1,125,000
Virginia	No District	Fauquier	Franklin	200,000
Virginia	No District	Goochland	Tellurium	200,000
Virginia	No District	Orange	Vaucluse	1,250,000
Washington	Chelan Lake	Chelan	Holden	12,863,125
Washington	Wenatchee	Chelan	Gold King	4,750,000
Washington	Republic	Ferry	Republic-Knob Hill	21,584,825
Washington	Orient	Stevens	First Thought	1,126,425
Wyoming	Douglas Creek	Albany	Keystone	189,000
Wyoming	Atlantic City	Fremont	Cariso	1,750,000

APPENDIX IV

BIBLIOGRAPHY OF SPECIALIZED READING AND
REFERENCE FOR AMATEUR PROSPECTORS

This list of books, reports, and maps is a personal selection from the many publications to which a prospector could refer for guidance in conducting or preparing for a prospecting trip. This list by no means exhausts the material in the field. This list will expand as your experience and continued research enlarge your knowledge of prospecting and mining. Some of these books will be available at the local library or the library will, for a small fee, request these books for you from other library collections. Some of the books and booklets you will want to own as part of your book collection for permanent reference.

BOOKS:

Adler, Pat., *MINERAL KING GUIDE*, La Siesta Press, Box 406, Glendale, California, 91209, published 1963. $1.00 paperback. (Specialized information to the Mineral King area of California)

Bateman, Alan M., *THE FORMATION OF MINERAL DEPOSITS*, John Wiley and Sons, 605 3rd Ave., New York, N. Y., 10016. Published 1951. $9.50.

Beiser, Arthur & Editors of *Life*, *THE EARTH*, (Life Nature Library), Time, Inc., Time-Life Building, Rockefeller Center, New York, N. Y. 10020. Published 1962. $4.95. (A good general book on the earth. No need to own, use the library)

Belden, Burr L., *MINES OF DEATH VALLEY*, La Siesta Press, Box 406, Glendale, California, 91209. Published 1966. $1.95 paperback.

Blumenstein, Lynn *OLD TIME BOTTLES FOUND IN GHOST TOWNS*, Old Time Bottle Publishing Co., 611 Lancaster Drive N.E., Salem, Oregon, 97301. Published 1969. $2.50.

Blumenstein, M. & B.S., *WISH BOOK 1865*, Old Time Bottle Publishing Co., 611 Lancaster Drive N.E., Salem, Oregon, 97301. $3.75.

Boericke, W. F., *PROSPECTING AND OPERATING SMALL GOLD PLACERS*, 2nd Edition, John Wiley and Sons, 605 3rd Ave., New York, N. Y. 10016. Published 1936. $5.95. (Very good)

Chalfont, W. A., *GOLD, GUNS AND GHOSTTOWN*, Stanford University Press, Stanford, California, 94305. $3.95.

DeDecker, Mary, *MINES OF THE EASTERN SIERRAS*, La Siesta Press, Box 406, Glendale, California, 91209. Published 1966. $1.95 paperback.

Dana, Edward S., *MINERALS AND HOW TO STUDY THEM*, 3rd Edition, John Wiley and Sons, 605 3rd Ave., New York, N. Y., 10016. $3.95.

Dana, E. S., & Cornelius, H. S., *MANUAL OF MINERALOGY*, 17th Edition, John Wiley and Sons, 605 3rd Ave., New York, N. Y., 10016. Published 1959. $14.50.

Editors of *Sunset Magazine, GOLD RUSH COUNTRY*, Lane Book Company, Menlo Park, California, 94025. $1.95 paperback. (A most helpful guide for tourist, camper, or prospector to lead them through the Mother Lode Country).

Griffith, S. V., *ALLUVIAL PROSPECTING AND MINING*, 2nd Edition, Pergamon Publishing Co., Maxwell House, Fairview Park, Elmsford, N. Y., 10523. Published 1960. $7.50.

Knoerr, A. W., & Lutjen, G. P., *PROSPECTING FOR ATOMIC MINERALS*, McGraw Hill Book Co., 330 W. 42nd St., New York, N. Y., 10036. Published 1955. $5.95. (An excellent source for details on claims, mining law source information, and prospecting kits)

LaGaye, E. S., *THE ELECTRONIC METAL DETECTOR HANDBOOK*, Western Heritage Press, 1530 Bonnie Brae Ave., Houston, Texas, 77006. $8.00 postpaid. (Well worth the investment).

Longwell, C. R., & Flint, R. F., *INTRODUCTION OF PHYSICAL GEOLOGY*, 2nd Edition, John Wiley and Sons, 605 3rd Ave., New York, N. Y. 10016. Published 1962.

Merrell, W. K., *GETTING OUT OF OUTDOOR TROUBLE*, Stackpole Publishing Co., Cameron & Keller Sts., Harrisburg, Penna., 17105. $2.95.

Miller, R. D., *MINES OF THE HIGH DESERT*, La Siesta Press, Box 406, Glendale, Calif. 91209. Published 1968. $1.95 paperback.

Morgan, Dale L., *PIONEER ATLAS OF THE WEST*, Rand McNally Co., 405 Park Ave., New York, N. Y., 10022. $10.00.

Morley, J. & Foley, D., *GRASS VALLEY AND NEVADA CITY*, Howell-North Books, 1050 Parker St., Berkeley, California, 94710. $2.50 paperback.

Nesmith, R. I. & Potter, J. S., Jr.., *TREASURE AND WHERE TO FIND IT*, Arco Publishing Co., 219 Park Ave. S., New York, N. Y., 10003. Published 1968. $4.95.

Paul, Rodman W., *CALIFORNIA GOLD, THE BEGINNING OF MINING IN THE FAR WEST*, University of Nebraska Press, Lincoln, Neb. Published 1965. $1.75 paperback.

Pearl, Richard M., *HOW TO KNOW ROCKS AND MINERALS*, McGraw Hill Book Co., 330 W. 42nd St., New York, N. Y., 10036. Published 1955. Paperback.

Pearl, Richard M., *SUCCESSFUL MINERAL COLLECTING AND PROSPECTING*, Signet Edition, New American Library, 1301 Avenue of the Americas, New York, N. Y. 10019. $2.95 paperback. (An excellent guide book).

Ransom, Jay E., *RANGE GUIDE TO MINES AND MINERALS*, Harper and Row, Publishers, 49 E. 33rd St., New York, N. Y. 10016. $5.95.

Ransom, Jay E., *ROCK HUNTER'S RANGE GUIDE*, Harper and Row, Publishers, 49 E. 33rd St., New York, N. Y., 10016. Published 1962. $5.95.

Savage, E. M., *PROSPECTING FOR GOLD AND SILVER*, McGraw Hill Book Company, 330 W. 42nd St., New York, N. Y., 10036. Published 1934. (A difficult book to find. Try used book shops).

Sinkankas, John, *MINERALOGY FOR AMATEURS*, Van Nostrand-Reinhold Books, 450 W. 33rd St., New York, N. Y., 10001. Published 1964. $12.50.

Van Bernewitz, M. W., *HANDBOOK FOR PROSPECTORS AND OPERATORS OF SMALL MINES*, 4th Edition, McGraw Hill Book Co., 330 W. 42nd St., New York, N. Y. 10036. Published 1943. $6.95 paperback.

Von Mueller, Karl, *TREASURE HUNTER'S MANUAL*, 7th Ed. This book is one of the best but is now out of print. Last price for this book was $6.00. Try used book shops or Exanimo Electronics, Segundo, Colorado, 81070. Von Mueller is the expert's expert in the treasure hunting field, and his book is a most valuable resource for a prospector or treasure hunter.

Wolle, M. S., *MONTANA PAY DIRT, A GUIDE TO THE MINING CAMPS OF THE TREASURE STATE*, Swallow Press, 1130 So. Wabash Ave., Chicago, Ill. 60605. $12.50.

UNITED STATES GOVERNMENT PAMPHLETS AND BOOKS:

All titles may be ordered from the Superintendent of Public Documents, U. S. Government Printing Office, Washington, D. C., 20402.

CAMPING IN THE NATIONAL PARK SYSTEM, U. S. Government Printing Office, (Catalog No. 129.71:971), $.25. (Lists over 2800 camping sites on federal lands).

GOLD REGULATIONS, Office of Domestic Gold and Silver Operations, No. T1. 10:G 56-3-969) $.15.

INDEX TO U. S. GEODEDIC SURVEY MAPS, U. S. Geological Survey, Dept. of Interior. (Can also be ordered from Dept. of Interior, Federal Center, Denver, Colorado, 80225) Quadrangle maps, $.50 each.

PLACER MINING METHODS, U. S. Bureau of Mines, (Report No. 2315).

PRINCIPLE GOLD PRODUCING DISTRICTS OF THE UNITED STATES, U. S. Geological Survey (Professional Papers No. 610). Edited by A. H. Koschmann and M. H. Bergendahl. A treasure house of gold mining history, locations of mineral districts, and types of geologic formations associated with gold mineral in the United States. A very valuable book.

PROCEDURES OF DESCRIPTIONS OF FORMS, Office of Domestic Gold and Silver Operations, (T1.10: G 56-4) $.10.

ROOM TO ROAM, A GUIDE TO PUBLIC LANDS, Bureau of Land Management. $.50.

STAKING A CLAIM ON FEDERAL LAND, U. S. Government Printing Office. $.15.

PAMPHLETS AND BOOKLETS FROM VARIOUS STATE AND PRIVATE PUBLISHING OFFICES:

AMERICAN MINING LAW, California Division of Mines & Geology, Ferry Building, San Francisco, California, edited by A. H. Richetts, (Bulletin No. 123).

ARIZONA ROCKHOUND GUIDE, Travel Promotion Department, State of Arizona Development Board, 3443 North Central Avenue, Phoenix, Arizona, 85012. (No cost).

MINERALOGIST'S POCKET REFERENCE, Colorado Assaying Co., 2013 Welton St., Denver, Colorado.

MINES AND MINERALS, RESOURCES OF CALAVERAS COUNTY, CALIFORNIA, California Division of Mines and Geology, Ferry Building, San Francisco, California.

PROSPECTING FOR GOLD ORES, Division of Mines and Geology, State of Idaho, Moscow, Idaho, (Bulletin No. 37).

WESTERN GEM HUNTERS ATLAS, *Scenic Guides*, P. O. Box 288, Susanville, Calif. 96130. $2.50.

There are in addition to the above publications many magazines specializing in mineral collecting, treasure hunting, and antique collecting. There are a goodly number of club and manufacturer's newsletters which contain bits of useful information. Also published are "treasure" maps which purport to show the location of lost treasure. These maps are interesting, but repeat often-told tales of so-called lost treasure, bandit loot, and the like. These maps are most useful to metal detector experts who can use the information as a lead to treasure hunting locations.

The first gold-hunters.

GOLD: Chemical symbol-Au
Atomic weight - 196.967
Atomic number - 79
Specific gravity - 19.3 at 70 degrees F.
Hardness on Moh scale - 2.5 to 3
General properties: Very malleable and
ductile; color is rich yellow to silvery
yellow.
Luster - metallic
Placement: Usually found in veins of
quartz deposits; often found in same
location as silver, copper and lead
deposits. The higher in silver alloy the
more silvery will be the color of gold.

SILVER: Chemical symbol - Ag.
Atomic weight - 107.870
Atomic number - 47
Specific gravity - 10.5 at 70 degrees F.
Hardness on the Moh scale - 2.5 - 3
General properties: A ductile metal which
is malleable only when annealed; Color is
white to grey-black in nature.
luster - metallic soft grey to white
Placement: Almost always found in vein
locations, seldom in placer since silver
combines in nature with many other chemical
elements to form varied salts. Silver
in vein or lode locations is usually quite
pure. Will be found in locations with gold.

The Most Productive Gold Regions in the United States.